MW00652038

GIS for Teachers

A Guide to Authentic K-12 Integration & Application

Christopher Bunin, Christine Esposito,

Barbaree Ash Duke, and Anita Palmer

Carte Diem Press | Dallas, Texas

GIS for Teachers: A Guide to Authentic K-12 Integration and Application

ISBN 9780986178221

ISBN 978-0-9861782-2-1

11272017

Dedicated to

the Esri Education Team & Jack and Laura Dangermond

for investing in teachers and student success.

You inspired us to be better educators.

For all online links and applications listed in the book, log into the book's companion site online.

All links there are clickable and current.

TABLE OF CONTENTS

Using GIS to Develop Geography for Life Explorers

Geography is a foundational discipline offering spatial and environmental perspectives needed to fully understand our lives within the context of Earth's ever changing physical and human systems.

Beginning in 1985 with *The Guidelines for Geography Education*, numerous curriculum frameworks, standards and assessment documents in geography, social studies and science education identified the important knowledge, skills and perspectives students need to be well informed and capable members of society (NCGE, 1985). Inquiry based teaching and learning, at all levels of education, is a vital common theme among past disciplinary and multi-disciplinary education documents and current projects promoting more and better geography education.

GIS for Teachers provides answers to several questions educators and civic leaders have asked for over three decades. What is needed in geography education? Who is it for? When is it needed? Where is it needed? Why is it needed? How to achieve it?

As you explore and use **GIS for Teachers**, keep in mind Susan Hanson's view that geographers offer a unique advantage to our inquiries. Notably, geographers consider 1) relationships between people and the environment, 2) the importance of spatial variability (the place-dependence of processes), 3) processes operating at multiple and interlocking geographic scales, and 4) the integration of spatial and temporal analysis. Hanson's ideas concerning the 'geographic advantage' are key to presenting and understanding past, present and future events and phenomena from spatial and environmental perspectives. She is emphatic about geography contributions to inquiries and reflections about significant issues and problems concerning Earth's changing systems and conditions of human well-being (Hanson, 2004).

GIS for Teachers is consistent with the views expressed in *Why Geography is Important,* "Geographic inquiry focuses on understanding complex local to global interactions of Earth's physical and human systems. Well-rounded geography education enables people to acquire the skills required to pose and investigate significant spatial and environmental questions and develops the ability to use maps, imagery, and geospatial technologies (Why Geography is Important (2nd Edition), 2012)." Humans live in many local places while being profoundly interconnected globally.

GIS for Teachers is consistent with the *Powerful Geography* project as it, "…imagines an inclusive geography curriculum that develops the capabilities of students of all backgrounds to realize their personal ambitions and make more-informed decisions about issues affecting their community, the nation, and the global environment. The Powerful Geography framework can be used to create teacher training guides that ensure pre-service and in-service teachers are better prepared to inspire a more diverse student population and broaden participation in the discipline and workforce (Powerful Geography, 2017)."

GIS for Teachers is consistent with the GeoCapabilities project regarding the pedagogies needed to advance powerful geography (GeoCapabilities, 2013). "Powerful Pedagogies enable students to: enhance their everyday experiences by extending and modifying their personal geographies; ask relevant geographical questions; see the world in a variety of different ways, informed by the academic discipline; apply what they have learned to new situations and places; be critical of sources of geographical information; analyze conflicting data and different viewpoints; consider ethical issues implicit in geographical knowledge."

What is needed? Teachers and students need to know that geographic knowledge, skills, and perspectives intelligently applied, are fundamental to reaching our personal and societal goals, and in attaining a higher quality of life.

Who should have it? Geography education should be a seamless fabric woven from many strands of knowledge, skills and perspectives stretching from primary grades to graduate school. Powerful and enabling geography should be available to all persons regardless of age and background. All teachers have a shared interest in advancing geography education. Primary grades are as important as university studies.

When is it needed? We need this aspirational, inquiry grounded geography education for teachers, students and their communities starting now and lasting into future generations. Sustainable environments and resource use require evidence based thinking and decision-making.

Where do we need it? Sound geography education and application of geographic knowledge as informed by the integration of GIS are needed in all communities regardless of size and location.

Diverse private firms and government agencies at all scales continue to adopt geospatial technologies to analyze and understand more fully their missions, structures, and processes as they Interact across space and over time. The adoption and diffusion of geospatial technologies will continue unabated for the foreseeable future.

Why is it needed? Establishing and maintaining human well-being requires extensive and deep knowledge across diverse fields of knowledge.   Geography is foundational and necessary.

We need safe places to live. Breathing clean air, drinking pure water, eating foods free of antibiotics, pesticides and herbicides and feeling secure in one's surroundings are all part of human well-being. Human development and success are diminished when such fundamentals of life are absent, scarce, or withheld. Individual well-being necessarily includes relationships with family, neighbors, and human communities existing in a context of sustainable interactions with physical and cultural environments.

How to achieve it?

Geography education should be a seamless fabric of data, concepts, skills, and perspectives with continuous strands stretching from primary grades through graduate school. *GIS for Teachers* is carefully crafted to lead teachers and students through the process of integrating essential elements of GIS into simple and ever more sophisticated inquiries and is applicable at every grade level. The recommended activities reduce grappling with technologies and provide opportunities to get at the thought processes behind producing maps and other visualizations.

The authors advocate building on modest beginnings and provide easy entry into GIS. Teachers may readily move from pre-created Story Maps to the complexities of Problem Based Learning at a comfortable pace for each teaching environment. Over time teachers and students can join in building activities together and design substantial parts of a multi-disciplinary curriculum. Important and necessary elements of student choice and voice are easily incorporated into activities.

Building the curriculum *becomes* the curriculum.

Now is the time to take advantage of the rich and accessible learning resources found in *GIS for Teachers*. The authors have provided readers with an exploration adventure with concrete and detailed guidance. You and your students can become *Geography for Life Explorers* by applying what you learn to daily life and by practicing it for a life time. Use *GIS for Teachers* to answer central and enduring geography education questions for yourself. Time to begin. Enjoy the exploration. Build the curriculum you want.

Dr. Robert W. Morrill

Professor Emeritus of Geography, Virginia Tech

Why GIS for Teachers?

Educators are life-long learners. We strive for student enlightenment, content understanding and critical thinking skills that transcend the individual subjects we teach. "It is therefore imperative for teacher education programs to adopt various strategies to guide, model and support pre-service teachers' development of technology based pedagogy, until it becomes an integral part of their professional growth" (Gao, Choy, Wong, & Wu, 2009).

The authors of this book knew that they had much to contribute to the conversation. If we, as a society, are going to prepare students to participate in the world of big data and global decision making, there is no better way to achieve these goals than utilizing geospatial technologies. Educating teachers before entering the classroom is the best way to make a systemic change than to provide this knowledge to students. Because there is no existing book written specifically for pre-service education, this book was created to empower pre-service professors to prepare their students with all the tools they need to integrate geospatial technologies into their curriculum and classes.

We believe that our methodical, pedagogical approach to geospatial technologies will change how all teachers see the content they teach. Connecting geography, global data, and real-world problems to the tenants of education will indeed change the landscape of education and empower future generations of problem solvers.

ArcGIS Online

There will be times in this book that you may need to save a map you have created. To do that, you will need an ArcGIS Online Organization account. In K-12 schools (public, private, home schools and informal education groups), ArcGIS Online Organization accounts along with ArcGIS Desktop and ArcGIS Pro and Community Analyst are all free. If you are not affiliated with a K-12 school yet, you can obtain the same ArcGIS Online benefits and learn how to operate and function within an organization account by signing up for a free ArcGIS for Developers account. Don't be concerned. You don't need to be a programmer to understand how to use this account, though if you do dabble in programming on the side, you will love this as well. The ArcGIS for Developers account is granted 50 credits per month which will be more than enough to accomplish any mapping goals you may have while preparing to enter the classroom.

To obtain your account, go to http://developers.arcgis.com.

- Scroll to the bottom of the page to the "Get Started Today" area
- Click "Get a Free Account
- Fill in your First Name, Last Name, and Email
- Click Send Confirmation Email. You will be emailed access to your new Developers account almost immediately.

To use your Developers account, go to ArcGIS.com.

- Click "Sign In" in the top right corner
- Click Content
- View where you will save maps and documents
- Click Map to start creating a brand-new Web Map or click on an existing Web Map name link

You are now ready to map!

Refer to Chapter 10 for access information and an index for the book's companion website replete with resources.

CHAPTER 1 – WHAT IS GIS?

Over the past several decades, as many of us have taught with GIS in our classrooms and branched into doing GIS outreach to teachers, we have met with resistance. The words, "it's too hard," "I can't get my technologist to load the software," "I don't have time," or "it doesn't meet my state standards," echo in our minds. Honestly, we have wondered if we would ever arrive at the place where teaching with GIS or teaching GIS would become mainstream. With the advent of online tools such as ArcGIS Online as well as the increasing opportunities of school connectivity, the introduction of GIS in the classroom is not only becoming more possible but more probable.

Image 1 Copyright ©2010 WPSU Penn State (formerly known as Penn State Public Broadcasting), an Outreach service of The Pennsylvania State University.

The term "geospatial technologies" emerged with the onslaught of geographic, spatial technology tools in the 21st Century. Even though Geographic Information Systems (GIS) has been around for 45+ years, 2003 brought it to the forefront with a shortage of workers in the field. In 2006, the National Research Council published a report called, *Learning to Think Spatially*. This report revealed research-based need for spatial elements within core content across the K-12 curriculum. Recently the Department of Labor declared the geospatial industry as one of the fastest growing. Appropriately, we should be integrating these valuable skills into education. Geospatial technologies include: online mapping sites such as ArcGIS Online (www.arcgis.com), or Google Maps (http://maps.google.com); virtual globe applications such as ArcGIS Globe (www.esri.com/arcgisexplorer) or Google Earth™ (http://earth.google.com); Geographic Information Systems(GIS) such as *ArcGIS(www.esri.com/arcgis)* or *QGIS (*http://www.qgis.org/en/site/); Remote Sensing and Global Positioning System(GPS) devices and applications that range from handheld units to NASA-grade equipment. The Geospatial Revolution Project at Penn State University, highlights geospatial concepts in an engaging manner (http://geospatialrevolution.psu.edu/). The Geospatial Revolution Project is an integrated public service media and outreach initiative about the world of digital mapping and how it is changing the way we think, behave, and interact. These technologies are used by many types of people: professionals, folks in their cars, weekend adventurers, school classrooms and more!

In 2014, in partnership with the White House ConnectEd Initiative, Esri committed $1B in ArcGIS Online Organization accounts for every K-12 school in the United States, whether public, private or homeschool. (http://arcg.is/1pvfNT0) In addition to the online software they donated, they also committed $1M toward the development of curricular resources to be used with ArcGIS Online. Esri partnered with successful classroom educators in the activity development process that resulted in ten cross curricular and cross grade level collections that encompass 142 activities, more than 150 maps and nearing 1000 data layers that have been created and "massaged" specifically for use in K-12 classrooms.

We mention these accomplishments, not as an advertisement for one company but rather the nod to the removal of numerous roadblocks to geospatial implementation in the K-12 classroom. The momentum is building and this is the opportune time to integrate geospatial technologies into instructional content that is required for teachers. In fact, today there are many ways to obtain free GIS software for use in our classrooms, Google, open source, and the like. For ease and the rich collection of classroom resources, we have just chosen to focus on the ArcGIS Online software and suite of activities.

WHAT MAKES A GIS?

Geographic Information Systems (GIS) is a modern analytical system of tools designed to help people solve a world of problems. According to Esri's website, GIS is, "A geographic information system lets us visualize, question, analyze, and interpret data to understand relationships, patterns, and trends." (Esri, 2017) GIS along with GPS and other place-based technologies exist in a symbiotic relationship across businesses, governments, humanitarian organizations, and education.

At the core of any GIS or geospatial endeavor is data. Geospatial data is information connected to a geographic element - a point, line, or polygon, that most often represents real locations on earth. This data can be collected on single map documents, symbolized, analyzed, and then shared.

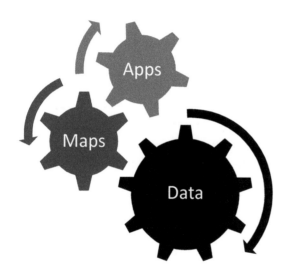

There is great power in visualizing things. Doing so on a map gives further context and reality to the words.

What's powerful about this kind of technology is the ability to connect virtually with place and space and ask questions about that place. Activities that may have started as an investigation to see your house from space can turn into an exploration of other elements that shape your world. This kind of exploration is particularly interesting to us educators as we seek ways to connect our students to content and teach our students to think beyond their borders, solve problems and create solutions for our world.

UNDERSTANDING ONLINE GIS

The Esri Education Team works tirelessly to ensure educators at all levels have access to professional tools and quality resources. The first stop in understanding what is available, Esri's Education Organization at http://Esriurl.com/k12gis. You will find several excellent resource collections.

The contents of the site:

1. Instruction Docs
2. Helping Educators
3. Community
4. Video Bonanza
5. Careers with GIS
6. Apps & Programming Resources
7. Maps and Apps Collection
8. Elementary
9. Partners in Education
10. Beyond Instruction

You will find a detailed index in the book's online Appendix I.

Image 2 ArcGIS Online for K-12 Education landing page

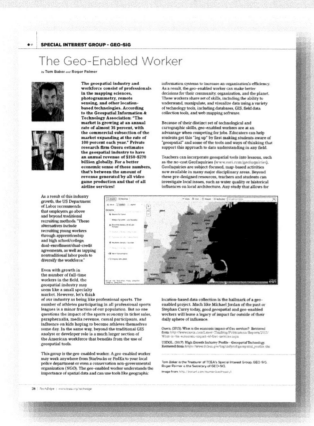

Tom Baker, Esri Education Manager, and Secretary of TCEA GEO-SIG and Roger Palmer, Science Chair in Dallas, and Treasurer of TCEA GEO-SIG wrote what we consider to be the compelling reasons for using GIS in the K-12 classroom. They identify the great need for geo-enabled workers in the 21st Century. Read "The Geo-Enabled Worker" online: http://bit.ly/2qFjJqQ . This article was originally printed in the May 2017 issue of *TechEdge*, a quarterly publication by TCEA (http://tcea.org).

1. GO TO http://esriurl.com/k12gis. EXPLORE THE RESOURCES. FIND THREE RESOURCES THAT YOU FOUND USEFUL AND DESCRIBE HOW THOSE RESOURCES SEEMED THE MOST HELPFUL.

2. READ "THE GEO-ENABLED WORKER."

3. WATCH THE CAREER VIDEOS ONLINE AT http://arcg.is/2sQVPMG.

4. WATCH THE GEOSPATIAL REVOLUTION VIDEOS ONLINE, http://bit.ly/2xXvQUI.

5. EXPLAIN HOW CAN YOU INTEGRATE WHAT'S HAPPENING IN THE GEOSPATIAL INDUSTRY AND CAREERS? CITE SPECIFIC EXAMPLES FROM THE VIDEOS.

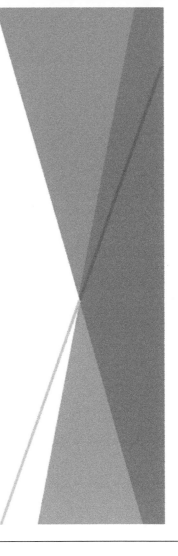

2

CHAPTER 2 – PEDAGOGY AND GIS

There are many facets to the integration and application of GIS in K-12 education. It is commonly thought that when one uses GIS, essential thinking skills are working together: critical thinking, analytical thinking, and spatial thinking. These skill sets are essential to navigate the world and be a global citizen. In this chapter, we will examine thinking skills, a continuum of geospatial resources, best practices, and how we reconcile geospatial technologies to meet pedagogy and standards requirements. We'll also offer exemplars from the core subject areas.

CRITICAL THINKING

The National Education Association published a guide entitled "Preparing 21st Century Students for a Global Society". The authors of the report identify four top criteria for students to be critical thinkers. (http://www.nea.org/assets/docs/A-Guide-to-Four-Cs.pdf)

- Reason Effectively
- Use Systems Thinking
- Make Judgments and Decisions
- Solve Problems

Three qualities that are repeated throughout the description of these criteria are: analyze, evaluate, and synthesize. These are the three 'higher order thinking skills' at the top of Blooms Taxonomy, though 'synthesize' has now been replaced with 'create' in the Blooms Digital Taxonomy. GIS, or geospatial technologies, is the tool of choice in almost every field of work today and have these skill sets built into its use (Sneed, 2016).

ANALYTICAL THINKING

The Global Digital Citizen Foundation posits that analytical thinking is a core skill necessary in preparation of today's students for tomorrow's workforce. It is essential that analytical thinkers must have proficiency in the skill sets: comparing, contrasting, applying, synthesizing, and evaluating (Crockett, 2016).

We all have experienced the flood of information coming at us every day and from every angle. Merriam-Webster defines "big data" as "an accumulation of data that is too large and complex for processing by traditional database management tools." What does "big data" have in common with analytical thinking? Aren't we just in need of storing that data? Yes, we need to store it but we also need to do something with those data. GIS technology tools aid in absorbing, digesting, and utilizing data to navigate today's issues. A GIS is designed specifically to help us to visualize patterns and perform analyses of spatial data from many angles. Students having the opportunity to use a GIS in school can train their minds to become adept at conceptualizing, organizing, classifying, and ultimately synthesizing or creating an action or solution to issues and problems.

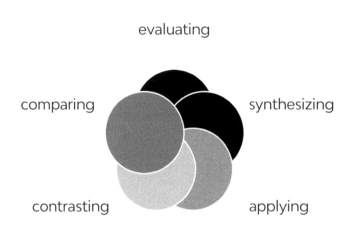

SPATIAL THINKING

Having explored analytical thinking and critical thinking briefly, what is spatial thinking? The National Research Council wrote in their 2006 "Learning to Think Spatially" study that spatial thinking is a combination of space concepts, representational tools, and reasoning processes. It continues to say.

"It depends on understanding the meaning of space and using the properties of space as a vehicle for structuring problems, for finding answers, and for expressing solutions. By visualizing relationships within spatial structures, we can perceive, remember, and analyze the static and dynamic properties of objects and the relationships between objects. We can use representations in a variety of modes and media (graphic [text, image, charts and video], tactile 3D models, auditory, and kinesthetic) to describe, explain, and communicate about the structure, operation, and function of those objects and their relationships." (Council, 2006)

Spatial thinking in concert with analytical thinking and critical thinking is the formidable trilogy of skills with which we must prepare our students to not only survive but to thrive in the work world of the 21st century. GIS and geospatial technologies are the key.

TEACHER PROFESSIONAL DEVELOPMENT

TPACK, http://www.tpack.org/, is a framework that builds upon Lee Shulman's 1986 contention that identified pedagogical knowledge, and content knowledge as necessary to be taught in tandem. Shulman's model highlighted the interconnectedness between the pedagogical knowledge and content knowledge realms and the new knowledge that results when these are learned together. In 2009, Mishra and Koehler added the technological knowledge realm to Shulman's model, acknowledging the critical intersection of technology into much of today's society. This resulted in the TPACK framework employed in teacher and student education research today.

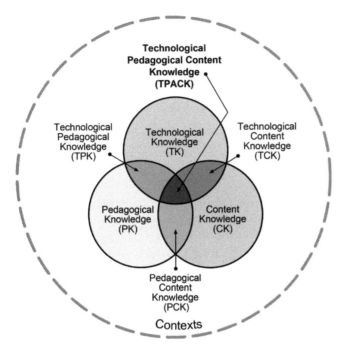

Image 3 Reproduced by permission of the publisher, © 2012 by tpack.org

"Technological Pedagogical Content Knowledge (TPACK) attempts to identify the nature of knowledge required by teachers for technology integration in their teaching, while addressing the complex, multifaceted and situated nature of teacher knowledge." (TPACK.org)

Martin et al explored implementation of TPACK in teacher preparation programs and proposed that "many teacher preparation programs are relying on out-of-date technology models and are in need of redesign. (2015) Dr. Martin's supposition was that for the most successful teacher education programs, it is essential that new teachers are prepared to use their digital native skills to integrate powerful 21st Century technology skills into their classrooms and teaching.

ESSENTIAL SKILL SETS: FOR CONDUCTING GIS PROFESSIONAL DEVELOPMENT FOR EDUCATORS

Technical Skills
- Files and their locations
- Fluent use of devices, software, and content
- Coping with the evolution of technology
- Troubleshooting

Teaching & PD Skills
- Identify appropriate GIS tools
- Use GIS across a range of curricular settings
- Engage problem-based learning activities
- Develop presentations about teaching with GIS
- Design hands-on workshops and training events

GIS Knowledge & Skills
- Spatial thinking and analysis
- Geospatial technology
- Creating and acquiring geographic data
- Using GIS to analyze data
- Using GIS to represent information
- GIS careers

In 2011, the Esri Teachers Teaching Teachers (T3G) staff, developed the Essential Skill Sets model identifying the skills that were essential for teacher educators to have in their training "tool chest" as they conducted geospatial education outreach. This model was highlighted in all subsequent T3G workshops and has been a core tenant and building block for geospatial education trainings at large. (Esri, 2011) The Essential Skill Sets model has been referred to as the "three-legged stool" using the notion that a stool with three legs must have equal length legs to comfortably sit or balance upon (http://bit.ly/2yTz8aF). Hence, providing professional development opportunities that afforded teachers to have well-balanced sets of Technical, Teaching/PD, and GIS Knowledge/Skills, would provide well-rounded teachers and subsequently well-prepared students.

Parallels can be drawn between the message of TPACK and the geospatial Essential Skill Set. The knowledge and skill realms align and there is the same "sweet spot" when the three "legs" are all the same length, maximum learning happens.

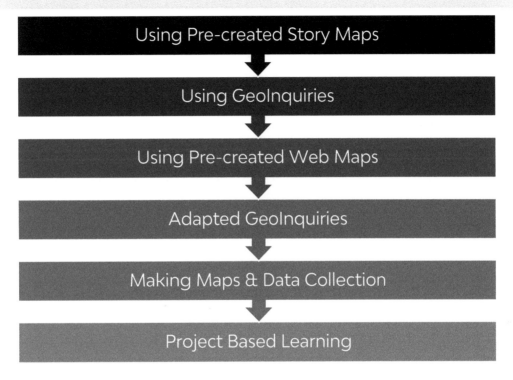

GIS tools for educators have developed over time. Teachers have many options to suit the diverse classroom environments. Over the past twenty years, geospatial technologies have been taught in the K-12 classroom in many ways. With the advent of purposeful materials to help teach GIS, we have organized these different teaching methodologies into a continuum. The continuum starts at the top with the strategy that might be most easily and quickly integrated into the curriculum. The methodologies located at the top require less movement of students, less tool knowledge, and less technology in the hands of students. As you progress down the continuum, the methodologies become more student-centric and hands-on, requiring more complex skill sets and planning.

If you have never used geospatial technologies yourself, you may wish to start at the top of the continuum so you can easily introduce the concepts to your students without disrupting the flow of your teaching. As you gain familiarity and comfort with the technologies, introduce activities from the vast array of materials that have been created for ease of integration into teaching. You may be surprised at how quickly you will progress along the continuum.

The following chapters will guide you through discussions and activities starting at the top of the continuum. Start thinking now about how you might implement GIS into your classroom.

WHY INTEGRATE GIS INTO YOUR CLASSROOM?

I want to replace:

- Sage on the Stage PowerPoint, notetaking with stationary images and slides
- Paper Maps and Worksheets
- Textbook Readings and Maps

I want to include:

- Time-Saving Web 2.0 activities
- Digital Tools that connect with digital natives

- Tools that will have students talking with their parents at home about "did you know...."
- A tool that will help introduce or review a topic in an interactive manner

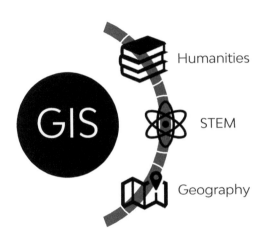

TANGIBLE CONNECTIONS

Regardless of your school district, state, or country, the subjects of literature, writing, science, social studies, math and technology are essential components of education. Students need tangible connections to their world and need to feel that what they are studying and doing has purpose.

As professional educators, our job is to show students how and why content is necessary. This call to action is also our greatest challenge. GIS offers real experiences for all subjects.

Exploring the globe is not discipline specific. Critical thinking is not exclusive to any one subject. We need sound curricular enhancements that cross curricular boundaries while teaching students to reflect, relate and analyze information. We suggest geospatial technologies as a single tool that joins curricular subjects and offers a sandbox for exploration and intellectual analysis. The following educators offer a glimpse into their past classrooms in their specific content areas.

GIS IN ENGLISH LANGUAGE ARTS

By Barbaree Ash Duke

 English Language Arts is centered on people, relationships and communication. Students seek a personal connection to learning. "Why do I need to know this?" How often have you heard that question? Admittedly, explaining the beauty of a gerund to secondary students is difficult. However, realizing that students NEED to have purpose in learning is a powerful insight. ...what does it take to educate [children]? What are the best tools for the 21st Century? (Duke, 2010)

STUDYING AUTHORS, LITERATURE, AND WRITING

Unfortunately, the ethereal reputation of literature class leaves students nonplused. "Dead authors and dusty books," as my students used to say, do not incite intrigue and inquiry. The books in the closet do smell musty and pretty much all the authors are, as Dickens said, "dead as a doornail." Studying authors is an excellent way to connect students with curricular content. English Language Arts (ELA) teachers have been introducing authors and explaining how their lives impact their writing for many years. Utilizing geospatial technology and place-related content gives us an opportunity to employ modern tools to catapult the past into the present. Connect Dickens to child labor, Twain to travel, Steinbeck to migrant workers, and Poe to tuberculosis.

Making literature meaningful keeps everyone happy. ELA teachers get to make their point about beauty and clever language while teenagers see purpose. Often, we English teachers don't have a choice, but more often we do. We're presented with a diverse collection in textbooks and novels to study. One of the most powerful tools in a teacher's bag of tricks is the thematic unit. Make choices that create a theme for students. Choose literature that has a tie to their century, even a small thread. Find literature that has connections to your part of the world. Place is a powerful connection. Where is *Our Town*? Was *The Red Badge of Courage* in a real place? Can we place Gatsby or Scout? Taking students to real places and having them draw conclusions grounds them and offers more for them to communicate.

Teaching students to write well is decidedly one of the most challenging tasks for the English teacher. Using geospatial elements in concert with reading resources offers some excellent proof and content for students to include in their writing. For example, a story or poem and a static picture of a starving Ethiopian child could solicit analysis, but students that experience a data representation on the map of this same issue have a deeper picture of the problem in Ethiopia as well as a more globally-centered perspective. They can ask intellectual questions of the map, glean answers that will lead them to analytical conclusions which they can discuss in writing. Students learn to communicate their argument or analysis in a more sophisticated way.

PROJECTS

Communicating and research are cornerstones of most academic classes. Student projects are an effective means to culminate assessment of those skills. I managed to get in about four per school year from my middle or high school students. English Language Arts projects might be centered around outside reading assignments, explore thematic topics, research projects, or be a collaborative work for two classes (i.e. English and World History). With a little instruction, students can make their own maps and include those with their research to make powerful map presentations or story maps. The use of tools like Story Maps or Prezi allow group work to be presented in a dynamic way that is more interesting for them and those viewing the results.

By Dr. Mike Jabot

 "There may not be a more pressing time for people to understand the role that science plays in their daily lives. At the same time, we have never had greater access to data about our natural world. This call to action and the opportunity to make informed decisions combines in a perfect partnership through the use of geospatial technologies." (Jabot)

As we seek to reform the way we both help teachers learn how best to bring science to life in their students' lives and how to empower students to be the change that we need as a society, we have been given a great roadmap for accomplishing this. *A Framework for K-12 Science Education: Practices, Crosscutting Concepts, and Core Ideas* (2012), helps us rethink how we traditionally have approached the teaching and learning of science. It shifts our view of science away from science content as the central focus of this work, to a greater focus on the science processes and engineering practices that are used to apply science content as well as crosscutting concepts that move our understanding of science content away from subject area specific understanding to the broader understanding of the interplay of these content areas.

In *A Framework* …. our views around science practices are moved from what most of have been introduced to, a series of rote procedures that we followed in our work, to a much higher level of practices such as modeling, developing explanations, and engaging in critique and evaluation of scientific evidence. Prior to the shifts that have been encouraged by *A Framework* … these were seldom if ever emphasized. Arguably, the most important of these is the focus on asking students to look critically at data that is presented to them. Developing the students' ability to evaluate alternative explanations considering the data, allows for the comparison and assessment of competing explanations in a way that not only moves students toward a "correct answer" but also helps them be able to analyze why the incorrect explanation is flawed. This helps fortify the understanding that science is in fact rooted in evidence not in opinion. There may not be a more impactful tool for students to glean, as well as evaluate evidence, than using geospatial technologies.

A measure of a students' true understanding of science may very well lie in their abilities to recognize the way science plays itself out across multiple scenarios and unique situations. At the heart of this recognition are the crosscutting concepts identified in *A Framework* …. Seven crosscutting concepts are identified based on their value across the sciences as well as engineering and their ability to serve as a scaffold by which students can connect ideas from across science disciplines in a consistent view of the world through the lens of science. With geospatial technologies, a number of these crosscutting concepts can be supported in the classroom in ways that have seldom been offered. As examples, the use of geospatial technologies allows students to investigate their questions based on patterns that exist in data across broad geographic regions or within their own region. Students can investigate the underlying causes and effects of phenomena through the use of geospatial data in ways that would never be possible without the analytic capabilities that geospatial technologies provide. There may not be a more powerful and comprehensive way of viewing the interactions between and amongst systems than geospatial technologies. These examples serve to give a brief introduction the power that geospatial technologies can play in bringing crosscutting concepts to life in the classroom and in the lives of students as they move forward.

PROJECTS

There are many very powerful ways that students have used geospatial technologies to expand and accelerate their learning. GeoInquiries serve as a straightforward way to introduce students to the use of geospatial technologies to investigate real-world science problems and do so in a very unintimidating way. The Global Learning and Observation to Benefit the Environment (GLOBE) program offers students the ability to collect ground-truthed data using scientific protocols and then to add their data to an international database which is informing the work of scientists in the field. GLOBE also allows the students to download data from this database to help shape their own research and to analyze these data using geospatial technologies.

National Research Council. (2012). A Framework for K-12 Science Education: Practices, Crosscutting Concepts, and Core Ideas. Committee on a Conceptual Framework for New K-12 Science Education Standards. Board on Science Education, Division of Behavioral and Social Sciences and Education. Washington, DC: The National Academies Press.

GIS IN MATH

By Dr. Bob Coulter

Arithmetic is the skillful arrangement of numerical information for ease of communication and comparison. It is a fun and enjoyable activity of the mind and a relaxing and amusing pastime — a kind of "symbol knitting." if you will. — Paul Lockhart (Lockhart, 2017)

As a former elementary math teacher, I have always been intrigued with the potential for GIS-enriched investigations to be a catalyst toward deep mathematical thinking, even among comparatively young students. My first GIS project was working with a student who had read about seasonal variations in the location of tornado strikes, which was in the news after one struck in suburban St. Louis in 1998. Nathan Strauss, then a 4th grader, decided to investigate whether the reported pattern was true, and spent the next couple of months collecting data in tables, organizing it in graphs, and making maps to show geographic patterns. The following year, he and his friend Nate Litz completed a 5th grade science fair project by collecting data on a range of water quality parameters in a local watershed (Coulter, 2000). Again, it was a process of collecting, organizing, and representing data on an issue that intrigued the boys. Several years later, I worked with 6th-grader Molly Patterson as she extended a project she started in a camp program I was running. She used GIS to analyze Census data which captured the racial and economic segregation in her community. These persistent and growing gaps were presented geographically at the 2008 ESRI User Conference in front of thousands of GIS professionals, and then laid bare for the world in a much more dramatic fashion in the summer of 2014 when these same tensions erupted in days of rioting in Ferguson, Missouri — just a few miles north of her home.

Each of these examples shows how geographic data can be used to explore what interests us, and communicate what we find. Underneath this process, there is a simple but profound use of mathematics at work. As noted in the opening quote, Paul Lockhart describes it as a process of symbol knitting, putting together representations of numbers in creative and useful ways. While many people think of math as a form of arcane wizardry best left to those geeky people who are "good at it," we do our students a great disservice when we do (Lockhart, 2017).

All too often, math class is an endless process of skill accumulation set out along pre-charted paths, in the absence of any concern for students' needs or interests. Success is measured in test grades and achievement scores, not in the ways students use math to understand and contribute to the world they are a part of. A well-crafted geospatial project can counter this, using math creatively to bring life to a project while simultaneously turning students on to their own potential to become a better symbol knitter by expanding their mathematic repertoire. In the bigger picture, this growth in students' 'mapematical' thinking promotes their capacity to be useful citizens working toward a thriving democracy, and it equips them with skills that will help them contribute to a creative economy. A win all around, I'd say.

GIS IN SOCIAL STUDIES

By Anita Palmer

 It is generally accepted that Social Studies in the United States comprises the following areas, in no order: geography, history, economics, government, civics, sociology, and psychology. There are other courses also considered as part of the Social Studies including anthropology, archaeology, philosophy, and political science, and religion. What is covered in the Social Studies depends on the state, region, or district in which it is taught. My thought is that the thread that connects all the content considered Social Studies or "social sciences" is the geographic thinking required to more clearly understand any of these content areas.

Aside from the fact that the breadth of content areas, why is the study of Social Studies important for students and why are geospatial connections important? According to Northern Arizona University College of Arts and Sciences,

> Thinking geographically means considering the ways in which physical space and place, proximity, movement or shift, and scale affect economic and political events and how past and current events can be represented in physical ways and analyzed in order to uncover spatial relationships. It also means considering how culture influences a place and how places change over time as a result. Helping students develop good geographical thinking

skills requires encouraging them to ask questions about the physical and cultural aspects of local, national, and international places and investigate the relationships between those places and past and present events. Equally important is the development of essential technological skills, such as mapping through Geographic Information Systems (GIS), which allow students to create their own physical representations to conduct spatial analysis.

As noted in the above quote, it seems as if the connections to mapping and analysis should be obvious, however, the breadth of Social Studies is one of those "good news, bad news" situations. There are so many ways that spatial thinking and analysis should be included in every one of the courses identified in the Social Studies. On the other hand, over the past 25 years, it has been far easier to point to geography and say THAT is where geospatial thinking and technologies belongs rather than including spatial thinking in all courses. One example, though there are many, is of a middle school educator using online GIS tools to teach an 8th grade World History topic to her students (many years before advanced ArcGIS Online tools of today). She developed a graphic tour (shown here) of Alexander the Great's journey that included topical graphics, readings, journal writings, links to imagery and video etc,

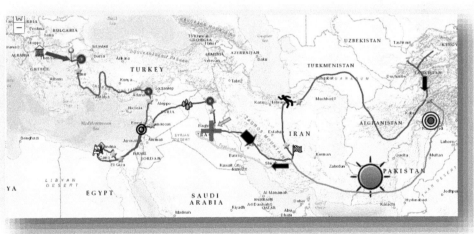

Image 4 Alexander the Great map by Tama Nunnelly, Middle School Teacher.

http://arcg.is/1GaPX. It has become an exemplar of the simple-to-create, yet powerful uses of an online GIS tool.

In the past, the challenge to integrate geospatial technologies into Social Studies content has been hindered due to the requirement placed on educators to introduce only topics identified in state and district Scope and Sequence documents. Over the past four years, the opportunity to integrate geospatial concepts into these broader Social Studies topics has been accomplished with the publication of the Earth Science/Physical Geography, AP Human geography, U.S. History, and World History, and Elementary GeoInquiries™. These 15-minute activities were designed for elementary and secondary educators to be able to teach their content with datasets created especially for history and earth/physical geography topics where data didn't already exist. Over forty-five activities are included in the social studies GeoInquiries™ collections and encompass over 200 interesting and important data layers for educators and their charges to more easily build their own maps and analyze those data.

There is still a world of Social Studies content areas that beg for geospatial connectivity and analysis but the four existing collections as well as Mapping Our World and Thinking Spatially, provide a strong start. In the future, beyond geography and history focused content that is currently available, I suspect that geospatial exemplars will emerge to introduce the use of geospatial technologies in those areas as well. We are seeing the tip of iceberg of geospatial technologies integrated across the breadth of the Social Studies due to the host of data now available as well as the knowledge that geospatial thinking can be done and is here to stay.

GIS IN SKILL DEVELOPMENT TECHNOLOGY

by Anita Palmer

 With the inception of geospatial technology K-12 education 25 years ArcGIS Online, the intersections into technology education have been less tenuous than integrating them in the content areas. "GIS" was more readily perceived as learning a new technology and was more broadly accepted by "Career and Technology" programs in school districts across the country (CTE, CATE). It still had its hurdles though, because it was looked at warily as a "new technology fad" that might come and go as had occurred with the many other "educational" technologies of the day (and still happening to some degree today).

In my technology classroom, I loved to not only teach GIS, but I enjoyed tying the technology to the content the students were learning in their other classes. I remember facilitating a multi-week project with my students where the students needed to come up with a question they would like to answer about any topic they were interested in or were studying; e.g. Sports teams, musicians, concert venues, traffic accidents, disease outbreaks etc. They then needed to do research on their question, gather data and map the data using GIS. I then required them to do a live presentation for the entire class where they described their question, methodology for creating their maps and what they learned in the process.

After the students recovered from the shock of having to present their findings, there were amazing outcomes from the project work with a lively and fun interaction between students. I will say probably the most difficult part of this assignment was for the students to come up with a question. They wanted me to assign a question and then they would find the "right" answer to give me. I declined and persisted in my original requirement. The learning that happened in these projects was not Earth shattering but I know was memorable to the students while setting the stage for more serious future educational endeavors.

In 2004, U.S. President George W. Bush, instituted his High-Growth Job Training Initiative. In a speech by Emily DeRocco, Assistant Secretary of the Department of Labor, she identified geotechnology, biotechnology and nanotechnology as the top three high growth job industries and that these fields were in desperate need of a trained workforce. This was the boost needed to provide the legitimacy and imperative for geotechnlgies to be taught in post-secondary programs but what it also did, was provide the need for geospatial technologies to be at least introduced in middle and secondary schools so there would be a feeder of geospatially aware students to enter the post-secondary geospatial programs.

Technology classes are a comfortable fit for geospatial technologies and I rarely needed to invent a scenario or simulation to teach them. It seemed there was never a shortage of projects that came my way for which my students could use their geospatial and database skills. I recall the state bird observatory finding my class just a few years after they started. This group had several years of bird data that had been collected by volunteers and at the time they knew of no way to aggregate and easily visualize the data. They heard of my students and their geospatial skills and approached me about having my class figure out a solution. One of my students created a database of their data, mapped the data in a GIS and trained them how to use the student created tools.

One of the large class projects that ended up making a significant difference for the community was the travel to and mapping by students of an 80-year-old house and property that was important to the history of the city. This property was acquired along with a house that was going to be preserved and restored as an office of the community hospital. However, the outbuildings were slated to be demolished in lieu of a parking lot. In conjunction with the state archeologist, I conducted a field experience for my GIS students to visit the property. Armed with GPS units, cameras, tape measures and notebooks, my students gathered and marked all structures and artifacts found on the property. The students mapped the data and provided a permanent record to the state historical society of this important part of the city's history.

Whether students are taken out into the field or whether they work in the classroom, geospatial technologies are an obvious fit. GIS has stood the test of time and is increasingly becoming one of the go to 21st technology tools in the technology classroom.

MAKE IT WORK

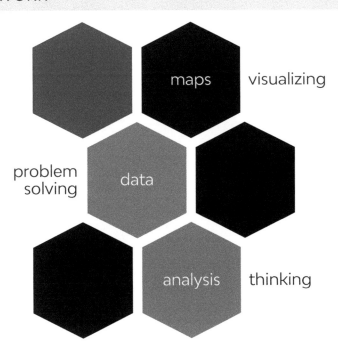

Some of the most amazing moments in our classrooms are unplanned. Regardless of your beautifully designed and planned lessons, you need to be ready for change. Each class has a unique personality, set of abilities and issues to address, and our well-designed, perfectly planned lessons do not work every time. Having a quick "go to tool" eases your "make it work" moments. Have some GeoInquiries™ in a folder ready to deploy. Create some maps for just in case. Remember what it was like to be in their desk. They want to connect and understand. Be ready to change students' perspectives, one enlightening map at a time.

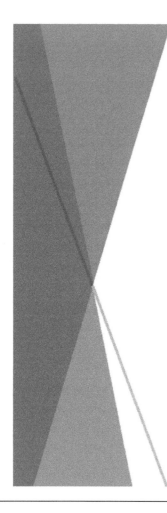

IT'S YOUR TURN TO FIND CONNECTIONS TO CONTENT YOU WANT TO TEACH.

DECIDE ON A SPECIFIC TOPIC.

THINK ABOUT WHAT GEOGRAPHIC CONNECTIONS THERE MIGHT BE TO THAT TOPIC.

LOOK FOR EXISTING MATERIALS IN ESRI'S GEOINQUIRIES™ COLLECTION.

CREATE A LESSON PLAN THAT INCLUDES A GEOSPATIAL ELEMENT.

GEOINQUIRIES HTTP://GISETC.COM/GEOINQUIRIES

CHAPTER 3 – WHERE TO START WITH GIS INTEGRATION

Your classroom instruction needs a spark. You don't have anything planned for tomorrow, you've got lesson plan block (like writer's block), and your school is pushing for technology integration and workforce readiness.

A colleague says to you, "You should try GIS?"

You give them the "death stare" that suggests, "Are you kidding me! My plate is full and I do not have the time to learn a new tool. Grades are due tomorrow and then we have parent conferences. It may be a cool tool, but my toolbox has everything it needs already!"

Such a response is not only common but also justified. Teachers are overworked and expected to stay ahead of the technology and instructional curve while often not being given adequate time to learn them during their regular work hours. Fortunately, several resources exist that allow you to seamlessly integrate GIS into your instruction with little to no training. All you need is a computer and projector, internet connectivity, and a web browser.

In this chapter, we share ways that you can immediately use GIS without a lot of training. These are free "take and bake" resources that, in most cases, were designed by teachers with teaching realities in mind. GeoInquiries™, Story Maps, and GIS lesson plans will make your instruction interactive, technology and workforce savvy, and have your students seeing patterns that aren't always visible with traditional tools.

GETTING STARTED

Any time you begin to use a new form of technology it can sometimes feel overwhelming. That is normal, but it is something that requires planning. The first few times, start with teacher-led activities. As you and your students become more comfortable with the technology, ask students to run parts of the lesson. Pay attention to the students in your class. Look for students who seem to have a natural gift for using technology and who aren't afraid to take risks. Later, when you're ready to implement student-driven assignments, pair them with students who are less likely to take a risk or who aren't as likely to embrace innovative technology.

WHAT IS YOUR PURPOSE?

What do you want students to know, understand, and be able to do when you are done with your lesson? Will this be a bell-ringer activity or will it be the focus of your lesson? Will it be teacher-led or student-driven? Is this something that will connect directly to your standards or will you use it to generate interest in the required content? Is this something you'll use to differentiate instruction: either to help remediate weaknesses or to allow students who've mastered your required content to explore relevant topics?

HOW MUCH TIME DO YOU HAVE?

The answer to many of these questions will be dependent upon the most important question of all: How much time do you have? GIS, online mapping, really can generate excitement in your students. As a new teacher, time management is often a concern. Not all resources (or classrooms) are created equally, so you'll want to have a solid plan for using a specific online mapping resources that considers all the factors.

OPTIONS FOR LIMITED TIME

- If you'd like to use online mapping as a bell-ringer activity, students should have a way to access the links easily on their devices. Students should be given a list of tasks to accomplish and/or questions to answer as they do their work. Because of the interactive nature of online mapping and the purpose of a bell-ringer, projecting the map on screen would not be an effective use of time or resources.

- If you'd like to make the map the focus of your lesson and have students learn specific, required content, you'll want to run a teacher-led lesson. This will keep everyone focused on the task at hand. For this kind of lesson, the teacher should project and run the lesson. While having students follow along on their own computers (assuming you're in a 1:1 situation) might seem to guarantee better student engagement, you're more likely to run into students who are exploring the map on their own and not following what you're doing.

OPTIONS FOR OPEN-ENDED TIME LIMITS

This is a wonderful time for a student-driven assignment. Here are some things to consider before unleashing your students:

- Before you get to this type of assignment, students should have been introduced and at least familiar with the basics, so their time is spent on your activity rather than trying to work out the logistics of the application.

- Decide whether you want students to work independently or with a partner. While it will depend on the nature of your class, learning should be collaborative and the discussions that occur as students work their way through assignments that invite exploration and drawing conclusions are valuable conversations.

- Know that the first few times you use a student-driven assignment, it's likely to take longer than you think it will. As students become more comfortable with the technology, they are more likely to take risks and show you things you didn't know were there.

- Build in time for exploration. Students are a curious bunch and they're going to poke around and explore - so it's better to account for that in your lesson plans rather than letting it derail them. It can be something as simple as, "You'll have five minutes to explore the map. When you're done, I'd like you to share one aspect that was interesting or made you think of a question." That can be a quick think-pair-share at the end of the five minutes or an equally quick class discussion.

- Make sure that your students understand the purpose of the assignment. Understanding what you want them to be able to know, understand, and do at the end of the day will go a long way towards focusing your assignment.

Using geospatial technologies or GIS in the classroom might sound like it will be difficult; however, with the advent of a plethora of pre-created resources, it doesn't have to be. This section will explore the continuum of resources to integrate geospatial technologies in your classroom.

PRE-CREATED STORY MAPS

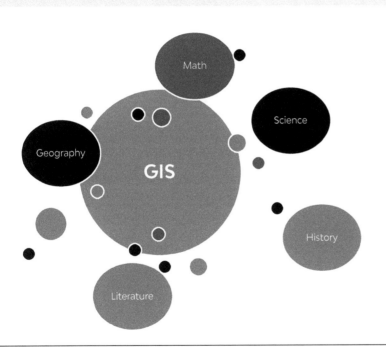

The first step along the GIS pathway is Story Maps. Story Maps should be considered along a continuum of familiarity with GIS. As a beginning tool, Story Maps require no software installation, password, or account. As you become more familiar with GIS, you will want an account so that you can create Story Maps and make them your own. As your students begin to see the power of Story Maps, you'll want your students to have accounts so that they can create Story Maps to demonstrate their understanding of a topic.

WHAT ARE STORY MAPS?

Story Maps, at their most basic, are a collection of data and multimedia to tell a story. The strength of GIS is being able to present complicated data sets to students in a way that makes it easier for them to see connections and patterns. Story Maps take a basic GIS map and allow the creator to integrate pictures and video to tell a more complete story. In addition to maps, pictures, and videos, text plays a key role in a quality story map. Whether you are showing primary-aged students basic maps with embedded videos or asking students to analyze complicated data sets, Story Maps can get the job done.

For many students, geography is not something that seems relevant. They're wrong, of course, but GIS and Story Maps can help them understand how geography weaves its way through their lives. They make geography more accessible to the student because Story Maps lay bare the relationship between geography and most content areas.

WHAT SUBJECTS ARE COVERED?

It might be easier to discuss what subjects are not covered. Pre-made Story Maps run the gamut from Nobel Laureate Immigrants, (http://bit.ly/DistinguishedImmigrants), to Ballpark Foods (http://bit.ly/BallparkFoods), to National Park Conservation (http://bit.ly/ParkConservation), to Ebola Outbreaks (http://bit.ly/EbolaOutbreaks), to Poverty in America (http://bit.ly/PovertyinAmerica), to Peaks and Valleys (http://arcg.is/2mSNxCA), and a host of others. The Esri Story Map Gallery (http://bit.ly/StoryMapGallery) allows you to search by keyword or to use their categories to help you locate Story Maps that will fit your needs. Don't be fooled that the Story Maps site is just a collection of whimsical map stories. These Story Maps provide powerful visual connections to all content areas.

A quick and straightforward way to pull students into the idea that geography influences more than they know would be to start with studying peaks and valleys (http://arcg.is/2mSNxCA), a Ballpark Foods map (http://bit.ly/BallparkFoods), or something similar that might spark their interests. For Super Bowl LI, there was a crowdsourced map (http://bit.ly/LIHouston) that plotted celebrity sightings during the week prior to the game.

Image 5 Ballpark Food map view

Middle school students can analyze the role class played in the survival rate of the Titanic's passengers (http://storymaps.Esri.com/stories/titanic/) and high school students can analyze how geography has impacted the current refugee crisis (http://bit.ly/TheUprooted). Though these are powerful stories by themselves, they are made more powerful by the Story Map format. The use of pictures, maps, and data details a story that could not simply be told with a spreadsheet and a map. While Story Maps are a great tool for middle and high school students, you should not overlook the opportunity to use them with elementary students. Whether you are introducing students to National Parks, using live cams (http://bit.ly/NPSCams) or showing them what the Ring of Fire looks like (http://bit.ly/SMVolcanoes) elementary students will get as much from a Story Map as a middle or high school student.

DOES IT HAVE THE DATA I NEED?

Story Maps are great but only if they have the data you need. While it's important to give students the opportunity to explore and poke around in a Story Map, it's vital that you have done the same thing. Whether it has the data you need or not, the map should tie directly to the purpose that you've set for the assignment.

If your goal is to analyze data, the Story Map should include more than videos and pictures. It should link to a map that will allow students to do analysis themselves or to utilize analysis that is presented as part of the story.

PRIMARY EXPERIENCE WITH A STORY MAP

First grade is not too early to start students with Story Maps. The National Parks has a Story Map with several live cams at their parks across the country (http://bit.ly/NPSCams). As students are being introduced to map features, directions, and being able to read numbers, this map hits a variety of standards. This story map experience was a teacher-led activity, which is appropriate for primary and remains appropriate until upper elementary as students begin to be more independent and

TIPS & TRICKS

SHARING LINKS CAN OFTEN BE THE MOST LABORIOUS PART OF THE ASSIGNMENT. SOME OPTIONS FOR SHARING LINKS EASILY:

- CLASS WEBSITE

- GOOGLE CLASSROOM (HTTPS://CLASSROOM.GOOGLE.COM)

- USE A LINK SHORTENER LIKE GOOGLE (HTTPS://GOO.GL/), BIT.LY (HTTP://WWW.BITLY.COM), OR TINY URL (HTTPS://TINYURL.COM/). THE LAST TWO CAN BE CUSTOMIZED.

- QR CODE

tech-savvy. Students sat on the carpet in front of the board. The teacher reviewed basic map features - title, compass rose, and a legend. She reviewed direction, as this map doesn't have a compass rose. Students were asked to choose the number of a place they'd like to see. At this point in first grade, there are still a few students who are learning numbers higher than thirty, so this was a terrific way to bring math into the conversation. As we called on each student, the student was asked to provide the number of the place he or she would like to see and the direction we'd have to go to find the number. Each new live cam brought a chorus of ooohs and aaahs from our first-grade audience. With each picture, we asked students what they were seeing - mountains, rivers, lakes, oceans, coasts, plains were all geographic terms we shared with the class. Students were eager to share what they knew about these terms, about places they'd been, and places where they'd seen some of what was on the board. Students had an immediate connection to geography - and to the world around them - because of the Story Map. Enough students asked if they would be able to look at the cams at home, that the classroom teacher added a link to the Story Map in her weekly newsletter.

UPPER GRADES EXPERIENCE WITH A STORY MAP

The use of Story Maps in upper grades - both elementary, middle, and high school would be more involved than the example given here. The goal in the first lesson was to introduce the technology and the vocabulary. In upper grades, a typical experience might involve asking students specific questions designed to test and push their understanding of what they are being asked to do. The questions would depend on your purpose.

Math and science standards in upper elementary ask students to read and interpret graphs. Many Story Maps use the embedded data to generate graphs. In addition to learning specific content, these maps can be used to reinforce math concepts. Ideally, the maps could be used in the math class itself so that students are given an understanding of why being able to read and interpret graphs and other data is an important skill.

In an upper elementary or middle school math lesson, it is appropriate to use The Uprooted story map (http://bit.ly/TheUprooted) to show diverse ways of interpreting data. This Story Map includes bar graphs and proportional symbol maps. Asking students to determine why data might be displayed in several ways requires students to dig deeper into understanding the math and putting math into a real-world context it often lacks.

When making technology a focus, always have written directions for students to follow. Creating directions using screen captures is an effective way to help students who might need a little extra support.

Image 6 Screenshot of "The Uprooted" Story Map

Advanced Environmental Science

Advanced Human Geography

American Literature

Earth Science

Mathematics

Upper Elementary

US History

World History

The second level of activities to use when beginning to integrate GIS into your instruction are Esri's GeoInquiries™, http://esriurl.com/geoinquiries or http://gisetc.com/geoinquiries. These activities require no software installation, no password or account, and were ***designed by teachers for teachers.*** These 15-minute activities use ArcGIS Online to help

teachers and students visualize and analyze geographic and map-based concepts for benchmark topics. Each activity contains professionally designed GIS layers, have been classroom tested, and are standards-based. Fifteen GeoInquiries™ have been developed for each of the following subjects: Earth Science, Elementary, English Language Arts, Environmental Science, Human Geography, Mathematics, US History, and World History. No prior experience with GIS is required, because each GeoInquiry™ comes with a fully developed GIS map, step-by-step instructions, guiding questions, answers, and how-to tips.

Image 7 Robert Chandler, a student teacher from University of Virginia, teaching with GeoInquiries™.

BEFORE GETTING STARTED THERE ARE SOME INSTRUCTIONAL DECISIONS YOU NEED TO MAKE.

- How will the GeoInquiry™ fit into your instruction?
- Have you completed the GeoInquiry™ yet?
- What's your classroom technology setup?
- What will your students do during the GeoInquiry™?
- Things you can do to make the activities better fit your instructional style and set-up include:
    - Have students write down their answers to the questions you pose on a sheet of paper and turn them into each other.

- Create a Google Form that contains the GeoInquiry™ questions and have students provide their answers there. To learn how to create your own Google form go to: https://support.google.com/docs/answer/87809?hl=en
- Use your favorite desktop or online PDF editor to consume a GeoInquiry™ and place it into a Word document, remove the answers to the questions and have your students complete the GeoInquiry™ on their own and then use the GeoInquiry™ map to review their answers. Cut and paste the questions into a Word document and distribute to students, or create a Google form in which each question follows the google form to answer the questions you ask.
- Devise some of your own questions to complement the pre-set questions provided by the GeoInquiry™. There is nothing stopping you from creating a customized set of questions to better fit your student population, curriculum standards, and personal teaching style and interests. Improvisation is encouraged once comfortable with the maps.

GeoInquiries™ can be used in each of these ways: teacher-led with one computer, one-to-one computer scenario, and customized integration that utilizes the data only.

OPTION #1 - TEACHER-LED WITH ONE COMPUTER

 The steps for running a GeoInquiry™ as a teacher-led activity require little experience with GIS. Simply print the activity, go to the map using your classroom projection device, and follow the steps. Explore the collection at http://esriurl.com/GeoInquiries.

OPTION #2 - ONE-TO-ONE COMPUTER SCENARIO

All GeoInquiries™ were created with a Creative Commons licensing to allow edits. Many PDF editors will allow you to save the text as a document and edit the information. In Online Appendix A, you have an example of an edit made to the US History GeoInquiry™ The Great Exchange.

OPTION #3 - DATA AND DEEPER DISCUSSIONS

A helpful aspect of GeoInquiries™ is that the maps can be accessed and used independent of the 2-page instructions. These are solid, flexible maps that contain powerful data. Below are a few ways that GeoInquiries™ have been integrated into classroom instruction.

- Visual aid to accompany a classroom lecture. Example: While teaching about the US Civil War the map can be brought up at multiple times throughout the unit to compliment a teacher's instruction of the many phases of the conflict. You can use the map to help explain secession, the early battles, the role of the capital cities, the importance of the Mississippi River, and how the war progressed to Lee's retreat to Appomattox Courthouse.

- Develop your own Activity using the GeoInquiry™ Maps. Teachers enjoy being the masters of their domain. There will be instances when you want to put your own stamp on the way these maps are used in your classroom. Go for it! Test drive the GeoInquiry™ and as you become comfortable with the lesson change the script to better fit your style, classroom, curriculum, and students.

- Take advantage of the NEXT STEPS and RESOURCES to go beyond the GeoInquiry™.

UNDERCOVER MAPPER

UNDERCOVER™
——— MAPPER ———

Over almost two and a half decades, the authors of this book have taught in the classroom, conducted teacher professional development events around the country and globally, and written volumes of curriculum. It seems that no matter how simple the online mapping tools have become, there has always been the need to take learners on an exploration of the geospatial technology tools they will learn. At the same time, work with elementary pre-service educators, reminded us that when introducing new technology skills in elementary, students at that level need to play and experiment with the tools before learning additional content.

With both of those factors in mind, Undercover Mapping #1 was developed to take the learner on an informal and fun tour of the tools needed to complete the Elementary GeoInquiries. These activities were tested by elementary teachers and their students and they were a resounding success. After some tweaks and minor revisions, Undercover Mapper #2 came along to take students on another adventure while gently ramping up the tool difficulty. Each activity ends with a fascinating "scavenger hunt" of amazing and fun features on the Earth. Take an adventure around the ArcGIS Online tools before diving into the Esri GeoInquiries collections and enable your students to become an Undercover Mapper!
http://gisetc.com/undercovermapper

PRE-CREATED WEB MAPS

After exploring the GeoInquiries™, perhaps you are concerned that the entire GeoInquiry™ does not exactly fit your state standards. At this point, why not use the interactive online maps, provided with the GeoInquiries™, Mapping Our World or Thinking Spatially, and integrate them into your lessons plans. Within these ten collections, there are almost 150 interactive online maps created specifically for the 4 – 12 classrooms. For instance, in Mapping Our World, Module 2, Lesson 1, (http://arcg.is/1z5MAqT) entitled "Earth Moves", there is a map that highlights plates, plate boundaries, and place motions.

Open ArcGIS Online and in the Search window, type in the content area that you would like to study. For instance, if you would like a map highlighting plate tectonics, type in plate tectonics and click on Go. On the left side of the screen, click on the Maps option. Today, the first choice is a map called Earth's Tectonic Plates published by Esri Canada. Read the details on that map if any are available. Decide if that map provides you with the content you are looking for. If so, click on Open in Map Viewer.

ArcGIS Online is a big, beautiful world of amazing content rich maps that are waiting for your input and use. Remember when you are searching and sifting through the maps stored online, that you always want to evaluate the author of the map via the details page so you can assess the efficacy of the map. The same rules apply to how you would evaluate a book or website that you wish to use.

STUDENT-DRIVEN LESSONS

Once you are comfortable with Story Maps, GeoInquiries™, and Pre-Created Web Maps the next logical step is to incorporate student-centered GIS lesson plans into your classrooms. Here are a few reasons to use full-fledged lessons:

- **Jazz up your instruction -** The lessons we share here are data rich, highly interactive, and will help you connect with your "techy" students or expose your "non-techy" students to technology. They will also help your visual and tactile learners.

- **Give your students the keys and let them drive (and thrive)-** The real "wow and aha moments" can happen organically. When you choose to use GIS, lesson plans you'll be providing valuable opportunities for students to learn leading edge STEM and workforce skills. The lesson plans we share here provide a nice balance of teaching content with GIS and teaching students how to use GIS to find answers and make decisions.

- **Develop your own GIS skills -** While your first experience using these classroom-ready lesson plans may be a bit bumpy you will really begin to master some of the basic and intermediate GIS skills and tools. As Charlie Fitzpatrick, Esri's Education Manager likes to say, "keep your knees bent." Which simply means remain flexible and have fun. Using GIS can be a bumpy ride, and it's so worth it. After completing these activities with a classroom of students and helping troubleshoot usual challenges your own knowledge and use of GIS will improve.

ADAPTED GEOINQUIRIES

GeoInquiries™ are customizable. They were created with a Creative Commons licensing so you can take the starting materials and adapt them to suit your class, standards, or content. You can access detailed instructions here, http://bit.ly/2sj3IIC.

We recommend *Mapping Our World for ArcGIS Online* and *Thinking Spatially Using GIS*. ***Mapping Our World*** was developed to enhance GIS learning for students of all levels, grade school through college, and to provide teachers with comprehensive and easy-to-use resources for GIS instruction in the classroom (Malone, Palmer, & Voigt, 2008). Another nice twist is that the instructions and worksheets are provided in .doc format so that you can edit the activities to fit your needs. The following listing provides an overview of each activity, http://esriurl.com/mappingourworld.

MODULE 1 GEOGRAPHIC INQUIRY

Lesson 1: The Basics - This lesson introduces the basic concepts and tools of ArcGIS Online. It will guide students in navigating the computer to find ArcGIS Online Map Viewer documents and data and acquiring fundamental GIS skills such as manipulating layers, zooming in and out, and identifying the attributes of geographic features.

MODULE 2 GEOLOGY

Lesson 1: The Earth Moves - Students will observe seismic and volcanic activity patterns around the world, analyze the relationships of those patterns to tectonic plate boundaries and physical features on the earth's surface, and identify cities at risk.

Lesson 2: Life on the Edge - Students will investigate the East Asia portion of the Ring of Fire, where millions of people live with the daily threat of significant seismic or volcanic events. They will identify zones of tectonic plate subduction and populations at risk.

MODULE 3 CLIMATE

Lesson 1: Running hot and cold - Students will explore characteristics of the earth's tropical, temperate, and polar zones by analyzing monthly and annual temperature patterns in cities around the world. In the course of their investigation, students will observe temperature patterns associated with changes in latitude as well as differences caused by factors such as elevation and proximity to the ocean.

Lesson 2: Seasonal Differences - Students will observe patterns of monsoon rainfall in South Asia and analyze the relationship of those patterns to the region's physical features. The consequences of monsoon season on human life will be explored by studying South Asian agricultural practices and patterns of population distribution.

MODULE 4 POPULATIONS

Lesson 1: The March of Time - Students will analyze the locations and populations of the world's largest cities from the year 100 CE through 2005 CE, describe spatial patterns of growth and change among the world's largest urban centers during the past two thousand years, and speculate on possible reasons for the patterns they observe.

Lesson 2: Growing Pains - In this lesson, students will compare the processes and implications of population growth in one of the world's fastest growing regions, sub-Saharan Africa, and the slowest growing region, Europe. Through the analysis of standard-of-living indicators in these two regions, students will explore some of the social and economic implications of rapid population growth.

MODULE 5 BOUNDARIES

Lesson 1: Crossing the Line - Students will explore the nature and significance of international political boundaries. Through an investigation of contemporary political boundaries, they will identify boundary types, compare patterns of territorial morphology (size and shape), and explore the relationship of boundaries to national cohesiveness and economic potential. By comparing 1992 and 2007 world political boundaries, students will observe the evolution of boundaries over time.

Lesson 2: A Line in the Sand - Students will study the creation of a new border between Saudi Arabia and Yemen. Using data from the June 2000 Treaty of Jeddah, they will draw the new boundary established by the treaty and ana-lyze the underlying physiographic and cultural forces that influenced the location of that boundary. In the process, they will come to understand how any map of the world must be considered a tentative one as nations struggle and cooperate with each other.

MODULE 6 ECONOMICS

Lesson 1: The Wealth of Nations - Students will look at three modes of economic production—agriculture, industry, and services—as the initial criteria for determining a country's level of economic development. They will add layers of data representing additional economic indicators—energy use and gross domestic product (GDP) per capita—and draw their own conclusions on how economically developed certain countries are.

Lesson 2: Share and share alike = Students will explore trade between the three countries participating in the North American Free Trade Agreement (NAFTA): Canada, Mexico, and the United States. They will look at exports from each of the NAFTA countries for the past 16 years and use this information to identify trends and to assess NAFTA's effectiveness. They will create a layout containing a map and graphs that support their opinions.

Lesson 1: Water World - Students will investigate changes that might occur to the surface of the Earth if the major ice sheets of Antarctica melted. They will begin their exploration at the South Pole by studying the physical geography of Antarctica. They will consider the consequences of projected changes on human structures, both physical and political. The assessment asks students to create an action plan for a major city that would be flooded in the event of a catastrophic polar meltdown.

Lesson 2: In the eye of the storm - Students will study Hurricane Mitch, the deadliest storm of the twentieth century, and the havoc it wreaked on several Central American countries. They will analyze information about the storm itself and about the region before the storm, and they will consider the storm's consequences.

Thinking Spatially Using GIS is a collection of activities developed to enhance inquiry and spatial thinking for upper elementary students. The following listing provides an overview of each activity available free of charge, http://esriurl.com/thinkingspatially (Napoleon & Brook, 2008).

MODULE 1

Lesson 1: Magellan Crosses the Atlantic Ocean - Students will follow the path of Ferdinand Magellan on the first half of his expedition's circumnavigation of the globe from Spain to the eastern coast of South America and across the Strait of Magellan to the Pacific Ocean.

Lesson 2: Magellan Crosses the Pacific Ocean - Students will follow the path of Ferdinand Magellan and his crew on the second half of their circumnavigation of the globe—from the west coast of South America, across the Pacific Ocean to the Spice Islands, and back to Spain.

MODULE 2

Lesson 1: Mapping a Zoo - Students will explore the concept of classification and how using categories can help make it easier to study certain things and ideas. Students will use GIS and work with a fictitious zoo to learn different methods of classification, create thematic maps, query data, and answer questions about what they see on the map.

Lesson 2: Touring a Zoo - Students will create a custom tour of the animals in a zoo. They will examine the relationship between features and attribute data. They will perform simple and complex queries to answer questions about the information on the map and in the database. The will use the information they collect to make decisions about what animals to visit on the tour and draw the path that the tour will take.

Lesson 3: Animals Around the World - Students will explore the concept of classification and animal habitats at a global level. Using data and information they have acquired, students will locate and identify a new animal to be introduced to the zoo. They will work with data from the World Wildlife Fund (WWF), including ecoregions, biomes, continents, and countries. Students will learn different ways that the world can be divided — geographically with lines of latitude and longitude or physically using biomes and ecoregions.

MODULE 3

Lesson 1: Early Settlement Patterns of the United States - Students will explore the distribution of human settlements in the United States. They will start on the Atlantic Coast and follow the movement of people westward to the Pacific Coast. As they follow the westward migration, students will use GIS to examine patterns in the distribution of settlements and will use different data layers to compare the locations of settlements to rivers, landforms, elevation, rainfall, and vegetation. Students will also examine some of the incentives for people to move west and some of the barriers they encountered.

Lesson 2: Patterns of a Growing Population - Students will explore the role of the United States Census. Using data obtained in the 2000 Census, they will examine population patterns across the United States. Students will profile their state and examine data on population, population density, and other interesting statistics on mobility and Internet access. They will use GIS to examine and interact with a number of graduated color maps and filter data to answer relevant questions.

Lesson 1: Finding Tornado Alley - Students will work with 10 years of tornado data for the entire United States to locate Tornado Alley. Furthermore, they will use three different approaches — frequency, intensity, and density — to identify Tornado Alley, the part of the country where most tornadoes occur. Finally, students will examine and compare seasonal differences in tornado occurrences.

Lesson 2: Analyzing Historical Tornadoes - Students will analyze U.S. tornadoes to compare some of the most well-known tornado outbreaks in history. Students will work with more than 30 years of tornado data for the entire United States. In this lesson, students will use the Fujita Tornado Damage Scale to classify tornadoes and identify the amount and types of damage associated with tornadoes of different strengths. Finally, they will look for spatial patterns and compare three well-known tornado outbreaks.

Summary

There are many ways to get started with using GIS in your classroom. The key is to do just that - get started! Reflect on what it is you are planning to teach or what you already teach. Is there a topic that is not instructionally sound or needs an upgrade? Are there topics you don't know as much about as you prefer or need to?

The resources highlighted in this chapter make integrating GIS into your instruction disciplined and seamless. In short:

- Take a tour of the topics in each of the GeoInquiry™ collections. Make a list of the topics that align with your content. When it comes time to teach the topic give the GeoInquiry™ at test run and identify the best way to weave it into your instruction.

- Check out the Story Map gallery and choose ones that you and your students will enjoy. Create a few questions to frame their experience and let it roll.
- Pick one of the ready-made lessons and turn your students loose. Keep your knees bent and we promise good things will happen. Your students will generate inquisitive questions, make spatial observations, and each of you will learn a tad of GIS.

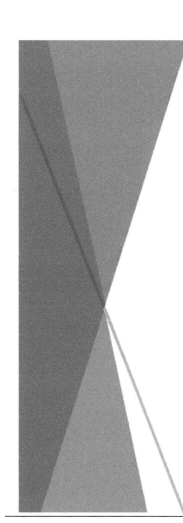

TEST DRIVE AND MODIFY A GEOINQUIRY, A MAPPING OUR WORLD, OR THINKING SPATIALLY LESSON.

DESCRIBE HOW AND WHY YOU WILL INTEGRATE THE LESSON INTO YOUR INSTRUCTION?

4

CHAPTER 4 - TEACHING WITH GIS - CONSIDERATIONS WHEN MAKING MAPS

What do you want students to learn?

One of the issues with technology in the classroom is that the technology can sometimes simply replace rather than enhance what teachers are already doing in their classrooms. Using technology for technology's sake can be a waste of time. The beauty of using GIS in the classroom is that students learn that maps are more than colorful polygons representing continents, countries, and bodies of water. They see beyond the map and make connections, easily missed otherwise.

Knowing the topic or concept you want to teach is a good place to start. Knowing what question that you want students to be able to answer is better. Questions can range from the simple to the complicated, can require no analysis or complex analysis. What are the big idea pictures you want your students to know; the things you wish they could just see?

By asking questions, you're asking students to share what they see when they look at the map. Rather than looking for the answer they think you want, students are more likely to take time to observe, to think, to ponder, and to analyze - even if they don't realize that's what they're doing. More importantly, students must use the map and its data to support their answers.

Let's explore some topics and guiding questions. These guiding questions keep students centered on the main purpose of the map, much like a thesis statement for a research paper.

Image 8 Barbaree Duke talking about GIS with students at a GIS Day event.

Topic	Guiding Question
The Civil War	Where did most battles take place during the Civil War?
Westward Expansion	Why New Orleans?
Ancient Civilizations	What did ancient civilizations have in common?
Watersheds	What is the path of a drop of water from the top of the watershed to the ocean?
Measurement	What is the quickest route from New York to Dallas? What is the most interesting route from New York to Dallas? How long would each take?
Flat Stanley	Where did Flat Stanley travel and what did he see?
Around the World in 80 Days	How long would this trip take today? Which trip would you rather take?

WHO MAKES THE MAP?

One of the most basic, yet vital, decisions to be made is who is going to make the map? Most people would argue that having students make the map is all about creating and therefore we should be aiming for students to make the maps. We don't disagree with the sentiment; however, that philosophy does not consider the many time constraints that teachers face daily. There are unquestionably times, when having students make their own maps, is the way to go. When the desired learning outcomes will simply take too long with students making maps, the best plan is for the instructor to make the map.

WHEN TEACHERS SHOULD MAKE THE MAP:

- You're introducing students to the wonders of GIS. You want them to see the possibilities, not grapple with the technology.
- You have x amount of time to teach y content, not one second more and that doesn't even account for the three unexpected snow days you had last week. When given the choice between teacher-created GIS or no GIS, err on the side of teacher-created.
- The first time you teach a lesson using a specific map. Unless you're teaching a GIS-focused class where building a map is part of the learning, we think the first time you use a map with your students you should make the map. It allows students to see how to handle mistakes and technology issues as they happen.
- You want students to understand the thought process behind making a map. Your plans involve having students make a map down the road. There are a lot of decisions that go into making a map and you want students to understand the thought process involved in creating a map. Use it as a think-aloud.

WHEN STUDENTS SHOULD MAKE THE MAP:

- Students have been introduced to GIS, they've seen how maps are created, and they're ready for the next step.
- Your content or unit is more open-ended. In this case, you want students to determine what data they need to answer a question and how best to symbolize the data. Having students determine what data might be needed is challenging and they may decide they need data that they don't have. The ability to problem solve and work around these problems is just as important as the content being taught.
- You want to teach GIS using your content. The ability to use GIS is a much-sought after skill in today's workforce. Teaching students the ins and outs of GIS may seem like an extra, but it opens doors that students might not know even exist.
- You want students to learn more than the content. Though soft skills are rarely found in curriculum standards, these skills are required in college and today's business world. When students create their own maps (or work with a partner) they are practicing real skills they will need in higher education and the business world: following directions, troubleshooting, problem-solving, and collaboration.
- Students are creating the data. If you've jumped all in on the GIS train and your students are now creating and/or collecting their own data, they should be the ones to determine how to best display that data.

It doesn't have to be one-size fits all. Who makes the map can be a matter for differentiation strategies. In Chris Bunin's classroom, he would work with a group of students on a teacher-made map while other students were busy making their own and working from that one. Students who might struggle with content but love technology find themselves leaders in the classroom. Giving these students a chance to lead in the classroom is a powerful strategy.

WHAT'S IN A MAP?

Now that you've done all your thinking and planning, it's time to make your map. ArcGIS will guide you and your students through how to make a map. You can take a tour that will help you make a map, style the map, or learn how to use the Living Atlas Layers (more on those later).

ONLINE ACCOUNTS

There are two kinds of ArcGIS Online accounts: public and organizational.

Public: Anyone can create a public account. It gives basic access to ArcGIS, as well as other Esri services. This is an individual account from which the user can make maps, search layers, and maps can be published.

Organizational: Public accounts can be used to make an organizational account and all the data will move from the public account to the organizational account. An organizational account gives users greater access to more Esri services, including ArcGIS Online advanced tools. To receive an organizational account, each school must apply for its account at http://www.esri.com/schools. Scroll down to the Offerings for Schools section, and click on "Free Software for Instruction" to complete the form.

There are numerous benefits to an Organizational account for educators. The account administrator has the usual administrator benefits: creating, removing, and resetting accounts, as well as being able to see everyone's work. Another benefit is the ability to make groups within the organization. Groups can be by grade level, by class, or within a class. This allows students to see each other's work and to collaborate with each other. Groups can help teachers organize their students in ways that make sense.

IMPORTANT NOTE

When setting up student accounts in the organization, in the beginning assign a maximum of 10-15 credits per student per year. See Online Appendix G for more details.

Explore the ArcGIS Online Use Strategies from Esri to get their recommendations, https://esri.app.box.com/v/agousestrategies. **See also Online Appendix G.**

BASE MAPS

The first thing to consider when creating your map is the type of base map you'll use. This is not a forever decision. It is easy to change the base map at any time. What makes one map better than another? It's often an aesthetic choice made by the map maker.

A.   **Imagery** - This map allows students to see what currently exists on the land but does not include place names. This is the map to use if you want students to be able to see cities, roads, waterways, etc. This is also a good basemap to use to show, in a big picture way, historical sites, and information. When zooming in on the map, current cities become more visible.

B. **Imagery with Labels** - This basemap labels countries, oceans, cities, bodies of water, etc. This is the map to use when students wish to make connections to contemporary sites. Knowing where something is and being able to find it on a map are important considerations. Both this basemap and the one above it allows students to see places as they exist.

C. **Streets** – Students may wish to map out a road trip, recreate a trip contained in a favorite story or novel, find local places of interest, give directions on how to get to their house, or talk about relative location. While the last basemap allows them to do some of these things, all that imagery can sometimes be distracting for students. The streets basemap allows students to focus on current information and locations.

D. **Topographic** - This allows students to locate physical geographic features without the distraction of imagery. This basemap also includes labels. This is the map to use if students would like to locate specific places or to see big-picture physical geography.

E. **Dark and Light Gray Canvas** - Almost a blank slate. While both basemaps include labels for cities, countries, bodies of water, etc. These maps contain little else. When students wish to pay attention only to the layers they add without the distraction of streets, buildings etc., either of these would make an ideal basemap.

F. **National Geographic** - This basemap gives you the National Geographic look. While it can look basic, as you zoom in on the map, it reveals topographic information, as well as roads, cities, bodies of water. Students can get a feel for mountains and valleys by looking at the shading on the map when zoomed in for maximum detail. It also includes a view of the oceans.

G. **Oceans** - The difference between this basemap and the National Geographic one is a lack of labeling on land. The focus for this map is solely on the oceans and the ocean floor including underwater mountains and volcanoes.

H. **Terrain with Labels** – This basemap provides a more 3-dimensional look to an ArcGIS Online map and the data layered on top of it.

I. **Open Street Map** – This basemap is a map of the world created by "crowdsourcing". It may provide more details on specific areas that might not have been concentrated on by official map creators.

J. **USA Topo Maps** - This basemap looks unimpressive from a distance. Its strength is in the up-close look. This is a very detailed topographic map for the United States.

K. **USGS Map** – This basemap created by the U.S. Geological Service is designed to be a fast basemap to display USGS topographic map symbology.

DATA LAYERS AND TYPES

Now that you have a basemap, you will need to add data to your map. There are three basic types of shapefiles: points, lines, and polygons. Points are used to show a specific place such as a city, town, or battle location. Lines are used to show rivers, roads, canals, and railroads among other things. Polygons are used to denote areas: states, counties, voting districts, territorial expansion, language areas, and land use. Imagery is any kind of picture that can be added to a map. This type of file is also known as raster data.

Creating your own data can be time-consuming, but there is plenty of data out there and more is being added every day.

FOLLOW ALONG TO EXPLORE THE INS AND OUTS OF ARCGIS ONLINE.

Go to https://arcg.is/1DeX9.

Click Modify Map at the top of the page.

TO FIND AND ADD DATA:

- Start by clicking the pull-down menu (down arrow) next to the "Add" button.
- Click "Search for Layers." This will default to **In: ArcGIS Online**. This will search data layers across the entire ArcGIS Online. (If the user would like to view only

Follow along sections walk you step-by-step through a process.

data layers created by people within their organization, Click the pull-down menu to change that to **My Organization**.)

- Type in your keyword *climate* -> **In ArcGIS Online.**
- **Uncheck the box next to Within Map Area** so that you will find data for entire world.
- Click **GO.**

*Notice the search returns over 3000 results. Explore some of these layers by adding them to your map. If you don't like a layer simply hover over the layer in the contents -> click on **More Options -> Remove***

Advanced Search

Sometimes you will be interested in searching for a layer based on the agency or person that published it. A simple way to narrow your search is to add the phrase owner: [author] after the key word you are searching.

For instance, let's say we just want find layers pertaining to *climate* that were created by a user account named *MappingOurWorld*. To search for these layers:

- Click on **Add->Search for Layers**
- Find **Climate owner: MappingOurWorld**
- **Uncheck the box next to Within Map Area so** that you will find data for entire world.
- Click **GO**
- **Add one of the MappingOurWorld layers.**

*Notice your search only returns two layers from the MappingOurWorld collection.

SYMBOLOGY

After adding data to a map, decide how that data will be shown.

- Make sure to click on the content button to see the contents of the map.
- Move the cursor so that it hovers over the layer to symbolize. This will bring up five icons* from which to choose. In order from left to right, they are:
    - **Show legend:** The legend for that specific layer.
    - **Show table:** Clicking on this will bring up the data table behind the map. It will pop up just beneath the map. This allows you to see all the data in a spreadsheet format.
    - **Change style:** This is where we will do most of our work.
    - **Filter:** Allows filtering of data so that only desired data is visible.
    - **More options:** Enables a variety of things, including removing the layer, zooming to that layer, and moving the layer up or down.

Note: Cloud-based software, like ArcGIS Online, is updated often. The tools and their appearance may change.

SYMBOLIZING: LOCATION ONLY

There are endless ways of symbolizing data. One of the easiest ways to start is to change the way points, lines, or polygons are displayed on the map.

- Click on the **change style icon**, which is the third icon from the left.
- Confirm Number 1 is set to "Show location only." Other choices may be available based on the data set.
- Beneath that, choose the drawing style by clicking the **Options** button.

- Click "Symbols" and choose the symbol and color that works best for the map story being told. Set Transparency and Visibility range. This will be a matter of aesthetics. If many points that will overlap when viewing at the world scale, it's best that the points not be visible until the viewer zooms in closer.
- Click Ok and then click Done to apply the changes made.

SYMBOLIZING BY TYPE AND VALUE

There will be times when you or your students will want to change the symbols of a layer based on an attribute. These attributes may be based on type data (ex. Religion, Language, Government Type, Active or Dormant Volcano), or numeric values (ex. Total Population, Income, Real Estate Values, Temperature). ArcGIS Online makes it easy to symbolize data based on these data types.

To change the style of layer based on type:

- Hover over the name of the layer you want to change
- Click on **Change Style**
- **Change the Attribute to Show <u>from</u>** Location Only to the attribute you would like to symbolize.
- Click on **Types (Unique Symbols)**

Create a map that shows the location of active, potentially active, and solfatara stage volcanoes.

- Click on **Add->Search for Layers**
- Find **Volcanoes owner: MappingOurWorld**
- <u>Uncheck</u> **Keep Within Map Area**
- Click **GO**

- **Add the layer, Volcanoes_MOW**
- Change the Style for Volcano Type
- Hover over the layer Volcanoes_MOW
- Click on Change Style
- Change to **Attribute to Show to TYPE**
- Click on **Types (Unique Symbols)**
- Click **Done**

if you would like the change the color scheme: Click on Change Style->Types (Unique Symbols)-> Options ->Click on the colored circles located to the left of the labels Active, Solfatara Stage, and Potentially Active. Click on OK -> Done

SYMBOLOZING COUNTS AND AMOUNTS

- Click on **Add->Search for Layers**
- Find **Constitutional_Convention owner: t3g09_BarbareeDuke**
- **Keep Within Map Area checked**
- Click **GO**
- **Add the layer**

Change the Style for Large Cities 1790

- Hover over the layer Large Cities 1790
- Click on **Change Style**
- Change the attribute to POP_1790
- Click on Counts Amounts (**Size**)

- Click Done

if you would like the change the color and size: Click on Change Style->Counts Amounts (Size) -> Options ->Symbols. Then Click on OK -> Done

Change the Style for the layer, US1790

- Change the attribute to TOT_POP (It is last attribute and you will need to scroll down)
- Click on Counts Amounts (**color**)
- Click Done

if you would like the change the color: Click on Change Style->Counts Amounts (Color) -> Options ->Symbols and change the color.

SYMBOLIZING POINTS: TYPES AND SIZE

- Click the **change style** icon, third from the left.
- Use the pull-down menu and use that to choose one of the fields to symbolize. In this example, use the city data for the first selection.
- In this instance, if you to show where the city is and see its relative size, click the "add attribute" button to add a second data field.
- After the second data field has been added, click the options button.
- The first option, Types (Unique Symbols), will display each city using distinct colors. Each dot will be equal in size to the others. The second option, Counts and Amounts (Size) will display cities based on the relative size of their population.
- Click on the option button under Counts and Amounts.

- This style section sets the parameters for how data will be displayed. By clicking the word symbols, the symbol's shape is changed.
- By dragging the sliders, it changes the quantity needed to display the largest symbol.
- The symbol size itself is adjusted by editing the minimum and maximum numbers under size.
- If the circles will be too large to see data beneath those circles, changing the transparency is an excellent idea. Setting the transparency at 25% is enough to ensure seeing beneath the symbols.
- You can once again set the visible range for your symbols.
- Click OK, Done, then Done again to apply these changes to your map.

SYMBOLIZING WITH HEAT MAPS

The Heat Map style allows you to explore the location and distribution of point features. It is a nice visualization tool that allows you to analyze where features are clustered together or dispersed. This technique is featured in the Protestant Reformation GeoInquiry™ to help students better grasp where the Jesuits traveled on their missions.

- Click on **Add->Search for Layers**
- Find **Volcanoes owner: MappingOurWorld**
- <u>**Uncheck**</u> **Keep Within Map Area**
- Click **GO**
- **Add the layer, Volcanoes_MOW**

Create the Heat Map

- Hover over the layer Volcanoes_MOW

- Click on Change Style
- Verify the Attribute is Location Only
- Click on Heat Map
- Click on Options -> Drag the Area of Influence so that it is set to Larger.
- Click Done
  *if you would like the change the color scheme: Click on Change Style->Heat Map-> Options ->Symbols and change the color. Click OK -> Done

*Note: When you choose Heat Map it will be the first layer to display above the basemap. Any other layers will draw above your heat map. Using this tool will take some practice and it will be worth it.

MAP NOTES

Maps should be interactive but not too complicated. Map Notes are the place to start and are easy to add to a map. They can be as simple as marking a spot or more complex to include a description and/or a picture. Bunin's favorite use of the map note is to attach a primary source to the map making both the map and the primary source a little more interactive than either would be separately. Adding map notes are as easy as adding layers.

- First click the add button.
- At the bottom of the pull-down menu, click "Add Map Notes."
- By clicking this, editing mode is accessed automatically.
- Instead of leaving the name as map notes, it makes more sense to give it a name that will help the viewer to know what area is seen.

- Keep the map notes template in this case. There are other templates, but the other templates may be more well suited for businesses and government.
- After clicking the blue "create" button, a menu will pop up.
- Pick the type of Map Note desired. Points are the easiest place to start. The style of points can be changed later.
- Clicking on one of the choices will bring the map back up. Click the spot on the map to position the map note. This place can be changed by dragging the map note to the perfect spot.
- When you click on of the point choices the map will bring up a new box. The information in this box will show when viewers hover their cursor over the map note.
  - Title: Give it a descriptive name.
  - Description: This can be a description or information about the point in question. It can also be directions for students to follow. Notice that the text in this box can be formatted using basic text editing choices. Links with more information can also be included.
  - The last two boxes give the map notes their punch. Pictures can also be added to a map note. Those pictures can also serve as links to more information. To add a picture, copy, and paste the picture's link into the first box. The image URL should end with an extension that denotes a picture (jpg, jpeg, png, gif). If it is a regular link (the extension would be .html), the picture will not show up.
  - To link to additional information to a picture, put the link in the second box. This link should be a regular web address. If you want your image in the map note to enlarge when clicked on, copy the same link into the second box entitled "Image Link URL."
- Some examples of pictures and links might include:

- Literature: The pin is located where a character lives and includes a picture of the character and a link to information about that character or a Google Doc where students can crowdsource a list of character traits exhibited by that character.
- Historical: The pin is located where an event took place. The picture shows a primary source document regarding the event. The link takes the student to further information about the primary source or questions they might answer regarding the primary source and/or the event.
- Math: Students are creating an itinerary for a road trip they're taking. Each map note denotes a place where they would stop to check out a tourist attraction and/or to spend the night. The link could be to a hotel or attraction. They could use that information to determine how much money they will need to take the trip and/or determine the number of miles between stops and how many days it will take.
- Science:

If students are creating a map for the first time, having them add map notes is a terrific way to get their feet wet and feel confident about adding information to a map.

BOOKMARKS

To create specific map places and map extents so that navigating your map is easier, bookmarks are the perfect place to hold those. This is especially helpful to introduce students to GIS. Bookmarks allow students to zoom to a specific view or location on the map, without wondering if they are in the right place.

CREATE A BOOKMARK

- Position the map exactly where students should start.

- Click the Bookmarks button.
- Click "Add Bookmark."
- Name the Bookmark. To edit the name of the bookmark, click the pencil next to the name of the Bookmark.
- Add as many Bookmarks as needed.

USE A BOOKMARK

- Click the Bookmarks button.
- A list of the Bookmarks for the map will be shown above the "Add Bookmark" button.
- Click on the name and the map will be repositioned at the site of the Bookmark.

ORGANIZING THE LAYERS

To add many different layers to the same map, which allows a variety of data to be shown on one map. It is important to note that the layers' order matters. The layers will draw based on their place in the list. Layers at the top of the list will display on the top, with the bottom layer drawing last. Keeping that in mind when organizing the layers on the map is important. As a beginning rule of thumb, polygon layers should be at the bottom of the list, line layers next and point layers at the top.

When you are using more than one of the same kind of layer, think about which features will need to be most visible. For instance, in the example below, this map has both state and county polygon layers. If the state layer is on top of the county layer, viewers will be unable to see the counties because the states polygons cover up the county polygons that are contained within the states.

There are two ways of reorganizing layers.

1. Hover the cursor over the layer to be moved until it is highlighted. Three dots will appear on the left-hand side of the layer name. Click the three dots and you can drag your layer to the desired place in layer list (called the Contents).
2. Click the three dots after the analysis icon that will bring up a menu. On the menu, there is an option to move the layer up or down (unless it is already at the top or the bottom).

SAVING AND SHARING YOUR MAPS

SAVING

 Save early and often. Unlike other online programs, ArcGIS does not save automatically. Using the pull-down menu next to the save button provides two choices: Save As and Save. The first time a map is saved it will need additional information to be filled in.

- **Title**: Name the map.
- **Tags**: This is a required field. The community can search public maps based on map tags. There are plenty of already created tags, but tags used should be useful to find the map in the future. A map can be tagged with grade levels, topics, countries, or anything else that will help to locate the map later.
- **Summary**: This is optional, but can be powerful. Write a summary of the map and/or the topics covered in the map. Teachers have many great ideas and carry them out only to forget about the last great idea. Putting specific information in the summary field is one way to remember the when and what of the map.

- **Save in folder**: Create folders in the Contents section of the Organization account right from the start. If the map ties into a watershed unit, create a folder called "watersheds and everything watershed can be saved in that folder so it's easy to locate again. It's much easier to be organized from the beginning than to have to go back to impose order amid map chaos.

Once a map is created and saved more changes and adjustments can be made to it. If a map is used to create a different map, be sure to choose the "Save As" option so as not to overwrite the original map. *Save As* creates a separate map that requires all the information that a newly saved map requires (title, tags, summary, folder location). This information does not transfer from the original copy of the map.

SHARING

Now that a map is created, it is time to decide if and how the map will be shared. Click on the share button near the top of the map.

Here, a choice is made as to who will be able to view the map. The easiest choice is to make it public. Anyone will be able to see it or search for it and the map can be shared by copying the link provided in the box.

Assuming an organizational account is used, there are additional options. The user has the option to share with the organization or just the members of a specific group. In the beginning, it will likely make sense to limit how public the maps are. Depending on what students plan to do with a map they create, a map may need to be public. In the case of a Story Map where the map is embedded, the easiest method is to make the map public.

CREATING A LESSON FOR STUDENTS

A simple lesson, teaching the physical regions of the United States, is often lackluster but offers an excellent way to showcase the power of GIS and delivers an engaging enhancement for students. This lesson uses the physical regions as described by Virginia's Standards of Learning for US History to 1865. This map is designed to help students see where the regions are located and to teach some very basic GIS skills. (If you are in a different state than Virginia, it is likely this activity will be found somewhere in each state's standards.)

FOLLOW ALONG TO PRACTICE MAPPING

STEP ONE: MAKING THE MAP

Setup the map:

- Go to www.ArcGIS.com
- **Login** with personal or school organization ArcGIS Online credentials.
- Click **Map**.
- Before beginning, click **Save**. Get in the habit of saving after each step so if there is a technical failure, it is only a small bit of work. Save early and often.
  - Title the map, "US Physical Regions."
  - Fill in the tag field. Suggestions include: physical regions, United States.

- o If desired, fill in the summary. Example: This map will help students locate and describe the physical regions of the United States.
  - o Choose a folder in which to save the map and click Save map.
- Choose the **Basemap**. For a map where students will connect the regions with their physical features, the Imagery, Topographic or Terrain with labels basemap would be the best choice. The basemap can be changed easily at any time.
- Click **Save**.

Add data layers:

- Click the **Add** button to find layers to add to the map.
- Click Search for Layers.
- In the top search bar, type *Physical_Regions_US*
- Use the pull-down menu to **change "My Organization"** to **"ArcGIS Online."**
- Click the **Go** button.
- Find the file named Physical_Regions_US by vbcpsgis.
- Click **Add**.
- Click **Done** Adding Layers.
- Click **Save.**

A single layer or service in ArcGIS Online can have more than one layer. This Physical Regions US file adds 11 layers to the map. When you click **Done Adding Layers**, the map will show the content area of your map.

This file includes:

- A layer for all physical regions of the United States
- Each of the nine regions has its own layer
- A layer for the rivers students must know

The content area shows you all the layers on the map. All layers are automatically visible.

- Click the box next to the names of the individual region names, as well as the rivers layer, to turn them off. (Physical Regions US: USPhysicalRegionsPlain should be the only layer with a check mark in front of it.)
- Click save.

Your map will have only the outline of the regions left.

Create Bookmarks:

- Using your mouse and/or the Zoom button, **zoom** in so that the focus is only on the Coastal Plain region.
- Click the **Bookmarks** button. Create a bookmark for the Coastal Plain. This will help students to focus on one region at a time. Create a bookmark for each of the regions, which will help students navigate the map easily once all the bookmarks are created.
- Click **Save**.

Add a Map Notes Layer:

- Click Add.

- Click Map Notes
- Give the layer a name
- Keep the Map Notes template
- Click Create
- Click Save

Create Map Notes for each region -> To add more Map Notes, click the Edit button so that it is highlighted in blue and the map is in editing mode.

Note: When in editing mode, to check to make sure Map Notes look the way students have intended, click the Edit button again to come out of editing mode. Put a check mark to the left of the Map Notes and then click Edit to go back into editing mode.

- Click on the symbol to use - either a stickpin, pushpin or cross.
- Click on the map to place the symbol.
- Title the pin with the name of the region.
- Use the description box to provide information on where the region is located and its physical characteristics.
- Find an image (or upload one) that is representative of the region and would help students better understand the region. Copy the link. Be sure the last part of the link is an image extension (.gif, .jpg., .jpeg, or .png). Paste the link into the Image URL box.
- To give your map a little more kick, use the Image Link URL to link to further information on the region. (If you aren't sure which one is the Coastal Plain, you can click on the different shapes until you find it.) This is a wonderful way to incorporate primary sources and/or videos into a map. A history teacher in Virginia has created short videos

that describe the features of the region and combined those with pictures. A link to his account: http://bit.ly/RegionVideos.

- Click the Edit button to come out of editing mode.
- Click Save.

Your map is now ready to use and share.

Share your map:

If your students have accounts and will be using them, you can share the map with your organization or group. Be sure the students are in the organization and/or group before you start the lesson. If your students don't have accounts, this map can be made public, but students will not be able to save their work. Click Share button. Select the group within your organization or everyone (the entire planet).

STEP TWO: CREATING THE LESSON

See Online Appendix B for a lesson, as written, is designed for a 1:1 classroom, but with some changes can be done as a teacher-led activity with a projector. This lesson also assumes the use of the imagery or imagery with labels basemap.

HAVING STUDENTS MAKE THEIR OWN MAP

With very few changes, this lesson can also be used to have students create their own maps. The power of this lesson changes when you put the students in charge of creating this map. They must find the pictures and the links, which means they are doing the research, having to sort through information and decide what is valuable. While this is always our goal in teaching, we also know that it's not always compatible with the time we have.

Again, this becomes an effortless way to differentiate a lesson by having students who finish early add Map Notes to the map they've created. Students can work together so that the more tech-focused students hone their GIS skills and the students for whom research is easier can also hone theirs. Together these students can create some amazing maps.

See Online Appendix C for a set of sample steps to give students.

APPLICATION 4

FOLLOW THE INSTRUCTIONS FROM THIS CHAPTER TO CREATE YOUR OWN MAP OF A KEY CONCEPT THAT NEEDS ENHANCEMENT.

- MAKE A MAP THAT INCLUDES LAYERS OF ALL THREE TYPES: POINTS, LINES, AND POLYGONS.

- CREATE A LESSON AROUND THAT MAP AND THE HANDOUT FOR STUDENTS.

- CREATE A NEXT STEPS DIFFERENTIATION FOR STUDENTS NEEDED EXTRA TIME AND STUDENTS MOVING QUICKLY.

- CREATE A RUBRIC FOR ASSESSING THE STUDENT WORK.

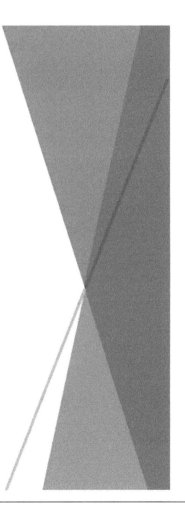

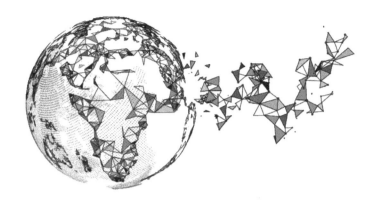

5

Every year Albemarle High School's world history classes have participated in a simulated archaeology dig in the school's courtyard. A pit of dirt is filled with all sorts of artifacts and students take on the role of the archaeologists. They dig, collect, and record data about the artifacts they uncover. In years past they entered their data into a Google form and created a report of their dig. This year, to jazz up the activity, they used an ArcGIS Online Geoform that allowed students to not only enter their research, but also pinpoint the location of the artifact.

As the information was entered in the Geoform, the teacher used the Geoform data to create a map. The next day his students were recording and mapping the data in real-time on the fly using a simple web page. Their entries were all crowdsourced and each point was stored in an online ArcGIS layer that could be analyzed.

GIS is empowering and exciting. By using GIS, teachers and students are no longer captive to "what you see is what you get" maps. Instead they can make maps that apply to their classroom, teaching style, individual student needs, and target specific instructional goals. Once teachers learn how to make a simple map using GIS, many immediately see the endless possibilities and wonder if they can create their own datasets, or even better, have their students creating data. The short answer is a resounding YES! While some of the datasets require technical expertise, most are not very technical.

A few of the common ways to create or collect GIS data for the classroom will be covered in this chapter.

TO CREATE OR NOT TO CREATE?

Before embarking on creating data, the following questions should be considered:

Why create this dataset? What will your students be able to see or do with this data? This is not a trivial question - Is this data really needed to improve instruction? Data creation does take time, but if it will improve instruction and help better support student learning, then go for it.

Does locational information exist for what you'd like to map? Does the topic or data contain locations so that it can be plotted on a map? The most common way to plot data is either by latitude and longitude or by address. If this information is available, then datasets can be created.

Besides locational data is there other information that can be mapped that will allow the map and data to be interactive and informative? Points on a map are cool, but additional data related to these points is even better. Take for instance volcanoes. It's one thing to show where volcanoes are located, but it's even more powerful to map a volcano's Volcanic Explosively Index (VEI) and include links to its Wikipedia page and image.

If the answer to the above questions is yes, then some simple data creation can commence following these five simple steps. For each data creation strategy, we will provide a sample classroom situation.

MORE THAN A DOT: ATTRIBUTES

The first step needed before beginning data creation is to think about the type of information needed to map, visualize, and analyze. In the world of GIS, we refer to the "what" as attributes. Attribute data is information about the points, lines, or areas on a map that is attached in the form of a table. When creating data, a few types of information should be considered.

Named (Nominal) Attributes- Nominal attributes is information that has labels or names (Hint - the word in French for name is nom) and doesn't have any numeric importance.

STATE	VA; NC; UT; OK; TX
GENDER	Male; Female
ZONING	Residential; Commercial; Industrial
US_REGION	Appalachian Mountains; Great Plains; Canadian Shield

Ordered (Ordinal Attributes)- Ordinal attributes is information that can be placed in some sort of order.

DISEASE_RATE	low; medium; high
CITY_RANK	Alpha; Beta; Gamma
CLIMATE	Cold; Warm; Hot
BLOCK	Young; Middle aged; Old

Numerical Attributes- Numerical attributes is information that can be counted. Examples of numeric attributes:

POPULATION	10,000
INCOME	$25,000
TEMPERATURE	72.2
AGE	35

TECHNIQUES FOR ADDING POINTS

There are many approaches to creating simple point data. In the following pages, we will model how to research and add points based on latitude and longitude coordinates, or by address. For each strategy, we will provide a sample classroom situation to help frame the process.

 FOLLOW ALONG AS WE EXPLORE THE INS AND OUTS OF DATA

LATITUDE AND LONGITUDE

SCENARIO 1: A STUDENT IS DOING A RESEARCH PAPER ON THE SEVEN SUMMITS. THE SEVEN SUMMITS ARE THE HIGHEST PEAKS ON EACH CONTINENT. THE ATTRIBUTES SHE WOULD LIKE TO COLLECT FOR EACH PEAK INCLUDES: NAME, LATITUDE, LONGITUDE, ELEVATION, WIKI_LINK, IMAGE, AND CREDIT.

STEP 1 - Open a the G4T_SevenSummits.csv file, http://arcg.is/2xiJg02 or create a new spreadsheet.

STEP 2 – If making a new spreadsheet, fill in the fields for cells A1 through F1 as shown below:

NAME	LATITUDE	LONGITUDE	ELEVATION	WIKI_LINK	IMAGE	CREDIT

STEP 3 - Go to https://en.wikipedia.org/wiki/Main_Page and search for Seven Summits. Use this site to compile information for each of the seven summits.

- First click on the linked text for Mount Kosciuszko, the highest peak in Australia.
- Fill in information for name and elevation (7,310)
- **To fill in the latitude and longitude**, click on the **Coordinates** link in the top right corner to go to Wikipedia's GeoHack site. Copy and paste the decimal latitude and longitude coordinates into the spreadsheet. The latitude is -36.4575 and longitude is 148.262222
- Fill in the Wiki_Link: Copy and paste the Wikipedia web address for Mount Kosciuszko in the cell for WIKI_LINK
- Add a link to a public domain image of Kosciuszko: For this activity:
- Scroll to the Gallery near the bottom of the Wikipedia page and click on the image "View of Mount Kosciuszko from south side"
- Right click on the image and choose Open in a New Window

- Copy and paste the address of the image from the new window (make sure the link begins with https://upload.wikipedia.org)

NAME	LATITUDE	LONGITUDE	ELEVATION	WIKI_LINK	IMAGE	CREDIT
Mount Kosciuszko	-36.4575	148.262222	7310	https://en.wikipedia.org/wiki/Mount_Kosciuszko	https://upload.wikimedia.org/wikipedia/commons/thumb/5/55/Kosciuszko01.JPG/1280px-Kosciuszko01.JPG	By Mass Ave 975 - Taken by Mass Ave 975, CC BY-SA 3.0, https://commons.wikimedia.org/w/index.php?curid=3798024

- Repeat this step for each of the seven summits and then **save the file as .csv** (comma separated value) file and make sure the students store the file on their local computer or cloud drive.

Use the Seven Summits sample file http://arcg.is/2xiJg02 as a starting place.

STEP 4 - Add the points to the map. To do this:

- Go to www.arcgis.com
- Log into a Public or Organization account

TIP: IT'S NECESSARY TO SAVE YOUR SPREADSHEET AT A .CSV FILE OR ARCGIS ONLINE WILL NOT READ IT.

IN GOOGLE SHEETS:
- CLICK ON FILE->DOWNLOAD AS -> COMMA-SEPARATED VALUES

IN MICROSOFT EXCEL:
- CLICK ON FILE -> SAVE AS
- CLICK ON BROWSE TO THE IDENTIFY STORAGE LOCATION ->NAME THE FILE
-> CLICK ON SAVE AS TYPE (BELOW NAME OF FILE)
->CLICK ON THE DOWN ARROW AND CHOOSE CSV (COMMA DELIMITED)
-CLICK ON SAVE

- Click on **Map**
- Choose Add -> **Add Layer from File**
- Browse to the file seven_summits.csv
- Choose Import Layer

STEP 5 - Symbolize to look like snow covered peaks. To do this:

- Click on **Change Style -> Show Location Only**
- Click **Options**
- Choose **Symbols** -> Click the arrow to the right of Shapes to change template to Outdoor Recreation
- Choose the Mountain symbol and change the size to 20
- Choose **OK**, **OK** again, and then click **DONE**

STEP 6 - Customize the pop-up information so that it only shows the name of the peak, the image, and links to the Wikipedia site. To do this:

- Click on the layer seven_summits -> choose the **More Options** icon
- Click on **Configure Pop Up**
- Keep {NAME} as Pop-up Title
- Click on the small **Configure Attributes link**
- Make sure only ELEVATION is checked in the Display column.
- Configure Pop-up Media by clicking on **ADD-> Image**

- Configure the image by clicking on the "+" symbol next to each of the fields possible. Since the name of the summit is already being used for the title, leave NAME blank.
- Configure remaining three fields to the remaining three fields:
  - Caption: {CREDIT}
  - URL: {IMAGE}
  - Link: {WIKI_LINK}
- Choose **OK** and Choose **OK** again
- Test drive the pop-up by clicking on any of the mountains.
- **Save the map.**

ADDRESS GEOCODING

SCENARIO 2: A GROUP OF STUDENTS WOULD LIKE TO CREATE A MAP SHOWING THE LOCATION OF THEIR SCHOOL DIVISION'S HIGH SCHOOLS. THEY WILL THEN WANT TO CREATE A DRIVE TIME BUFFER OF 30 MINUTES TO SEE HOW MUCH OF THE DIVISION LIVES OUTSIDE THESE AREAS. IN THIS SCENARIO, WE WILL USE ALBEMARLE COUNTY, VIRGINIA AS THE CASE STUDY. THE ATTRIBUTES TO COLLECT ARE: NAME, LEVEL, ADDRESS, CITY, STATE, ZIP CODE.

STEP 1 - Open a spreadsheet using Microsoft Excel or Google sheets.

STEP 2 - Fill in the fields for cells A1 through F1 as shown below:

NAME	LEVEL	ADDRESS	CITY	STATE	ZIP_CODE

STEP 3 - Find the address for each of the school division's schools and enter the information. Below is the information found for Albemarle High School in Charlottesville, VA. (You may add your own list of schools here.)

NAME	LEVEL	ADDRESS	CITY	STATE	ZIP_CODE
Albemarle	High	2775 Hydraulic Road	Charlottesville	VA	22920
Western Albemarle	High	5941 Rockfish Gap Turnpike	Crozet	VA	22932
Monticello	High	1400 Independence Way	Charlottesville	VA	22902
Murray	High	1200 Forest St	Charlottesville	VA	22903

Repeat this step for each of the schools and save the file as a .CSV file. In the case of Albemarle County there are four high schools.

STEP 4 - Add the points to the map.

- Go to www.arcgis.com
- Log into an organization account
- Click on **Map**
- Choose Add -> **Add Layer from File**
- Browse to the file containing school addresses.
- Click open and then Import layer.

- Verify that Country is United States and that ADDRESS, CITY, STATE, and ZIP are chosen in the Location Fields.
- Choose Add Layer

STEP 5 - Symbolize the schools based on location only.

- Click on Change Style -> **Show Location Only**
- Click on **Options.**
- Choose on the arrow to the right of Spaces to change to People Places.
- Choose the Red School house and change the size to 16.
- Choose **OK**, **OK** again and then click **DONE**

STEP 6 - Now let's create drive time rings (Note: This functionality requires an ArcGIS Online Organizational account that allows users to perform analysis.)

- Click on Analysis -> Use Proximity -> Create Drive-Time Areas
- Choose AddressGeoCode as the point layer to calculate drive time.
- Change the driving time to 30 minutes.
- Choose Dissolve so that drive time that overlap don't get duplicated.
- Name the output file Drive time (30 minutes) with your initials after the name (the name must be unique).
- Click on the small **Show Credits link** to check your credit consumption with this process.
- Choose **Run Analysis**. This may take a few minutes.
- When it finishes running a drive time ring of showing all areas within 30 minutes is calculated.

Think about all the points that could be added to map based on address whether it be by full address, or city and state. What would be most interesting to map: cities, super bowl locations, types of stores in your town? With ArcGIS Online, the locations can be mapped in a snap!

COLLABORATIVE DATA CREATION: CROWDSOURCING

USING GOOGLE SHEETS

Collaboration on data collection is a lot of fun and not hard to do. Each of the data creation techniques shared can easily be crowdsourced using Google Docs. Simply identify the data that students wish to create and share a Google Sheet that contains the attributes to collect. The most challenging piece is managing the data so that students do not duplicate or overwrite the data being collected.

Once the data is collected by latitude/longitude or by address export the file as a CSV file and follow the same directions provided in the previous sections.

EDITABLE FEATURE SERVICES

WHAT IS AN EDITABLE FEATURE SERVICE?

An editable feature service is a GIS layer that can be edited by multiple people at one time in the form an ArcGIS Online Web Map, GeoForm, or using the ArcGIS Collector App.

WHEN SHOULD AN EDITABLE FEATURE SERVICE BE USED?

When flexible data collection is needed. This may include: collecting points of interest or information from all students at one time; sending students out into the community or around campus to collect and add data (cell phone reception, public opinion, survey data, collecting inventory (trees, light posts, trash, etc).

WHAT'S THE DIFFERENCE IN COLLECTING DATA USING AN ARCGIS ONLINE MAP, GEOFORM, OR COLLECTOR APP?

ArcGIS Online Map – add an editable feature service to an ArcGIS Online map and share the map with students (share to everyone or share it to a group). Then, students add data by clicking on the edit button in the map and add data points.

GeoForm - Geoform is a configurable app template for form-based data editing of a Feature Service. This application allows users to enter data through a form instead of a map's pop-up while leveraging the power of the Web Map and editable Feature Services. This app geo-enables data and workflows by lowering the barrier of entry for completing simple tasks. Useful to collect new point data from a large audience of non-technical staff or members of the community (Source: Esri)

Collector for ArcGIS - Collect and update data in the field, log current location, and put the data captured to work to make more informed and timely decisions. Use maps anywhere to ground truth the data, make observations, and respond to events. The efficiency of the field workforce and the accuracy of your GIS will be improved. Download the FREE Collector for ArcGIS app from the AppStore, Google Play, or the Windows Store. The app can be downloaded to a smartphone or tablet, but for the app to work properly the device must use cellular data such as 3G, 4G, or LTE. *Android and iOS only (Source: Esri)

Survey 123 – The smart survey tool allows you to very easily design surveys on the web with predefined questions that use logic and provide easy-to-fill answers, embedded audio and images. The beauty of Survey 123 is that it combines the power of smart forms and geography! Data captured in Survey123 for ArcGIS is immediately available in the ArcGIS Online to understand your data and communicate and share your work. (Esri)

SCENARIO 3: YOU ARE TEACHING ABOUT THE COLUMBIAN EXCHANGE AND WOULD LIKE TO CREATE AN ACTIVITY IN WHICH YOUR STUDENTS RESEARCH AND PLOT THE INGREDIENTS FOR A RECIPE OF THEIR CHOICE. YOU WILL THEN USE THE MAP TO HELP DISCUSS HOW GLOBAL FOOD IN AMERICA IS TODAY. YOUR STUDENTS WILL BE ABLE TO PLOT THE INGREDIENT LOCATIONS EITHER USING AN ARCGIS ONLINE MAP OR USING A GEOFORM.

Create a .CSV file creating the table of information needed to collect the data. The table must have either latitude and longitude fields or at least two address location fields (City and State). ArcGIS Online requires these fields simply as placeholders. An example of fields is below. Save this file as .CSV.

-

USING LATITUDE AND LONGITUDE

INITIALS	RECIPE	INGREDIENT	LATITUDE	LONGITUDE

USING ADDRESS

INITIALS	RECIPE	INGREDIENT	CITY	STATE

Add the .CSV file into ArcGIS Online

- **Log into ArcGIS Online** (www.arcgis.com) using an Organization Account.
- Choose **Content** and create a folder for the project to help keep files organized.
  - ○ Click on **New** and name a folder
  - ○ Click on **Add Item**
  - ○ Open the new folder and click on Add Item -> From My Computer
  - ○ **Browse** to the .CSV file created and click on the **Choose File** icon and choose **Open**
  - ○ Fill in the required information before adding the item. **Make sure to choose to:**
  - ○ Publish this file as a hosted layer
  - ○ Locate features using: Latitude/Longitude or Address depending on whether latitude and longitude or address fields in .CSV file were used.

- Once the file is added scroll down to **Layers** and click to **Enable Attachments**. Choose the tab, From Existing Layer.
- Click on **Share** and choose the groups to share the file with. To avoid students needing to log-in, choose **Everyone.**
- Create an Editable Feature Service from the file added. To do this:

  - ○ Click on My Content and click on the folder with the uploaded file.
  - ○ Click on Create -> Feature Layer
  - ○ Choose from Existing Layer*

*Note: ArcGIS Online has many templates that exist that may fit what is being studied. Click on **From Template** to use a pre-made file.*

- **Search** for the file that has been created.
- Choose **Create** and click **Next**
- **Zoom in** to set the map extent for the new hosted layer.
- Choose **Next**
- Specify a title, tags, and summary for the hosted layer.
- Choose Done**If the process takes a long time, click cancel and redo the step. It may have gotten hung up.
- Once the feature service has been created choose Open in Map Viewer
- Change the style of the layer to Show location only and choose the symbol to use for the point data being collected. Be sure to click on Done.
- Save the Map and give the map a title, tags, and summary.

SHARE THE MAP.SHARING WITH STUDENTS VIA WEBLINK

By saving the feature service in a map and sharing it, students can add data directly to the map by giving them the "Link to this Map." Make sure the share settings are set so that students can access the map with or without logging into ArcGIS Online.

SHARING WITH STUDENTS VIA GEOFORM

Once the map is created, click on **Share** and choose to **Create a Web App.** Click on the **Collect/Edit Data** tab and choose **GeoForm**. Follow the steps to create the Geoform. You can then share the web link to have students collect data by completing a form and putting their data point on the map. **Make sure the share settings are set so that students can access the map with or without logging into ArcGIS Online.**

To see a live example of the Colombian Exchange activity using a GeoForm, go to this link, http://arcg.is/2qXlwdr. It was completed by a typical World History class with the symbology set to show location. It's an excellent conversation starter and shows how the past is a lens to today.

Note - the Geoform map is tied to the map you saved and shared as a Geoform. If you go back to the original map made to share the Editable Feature Service the symbols and filter the layer can be changed based on the students' initials. You can also change the style of the points to the Heat Map style. The "hottest" areas align with the world's agricultural hearths.

COLLECTING DATA USING COLLECTOR FOR ARCGIS

Students will need to have the Collector for ArcGIS app on their phone or device. Once the map is saved and shared properly have students **open Collector for ArcGIS, log in**, and search for the map that has been already created and saved. Then model how to collect data using the app. The map **must be shared with a group*** that all people collecting data belong to. If the map is not shared with a specific group your students will not be able to access the map using Collector for ArcGIS.

CREATING A GROUP

To create a group:

- Log into ArcGIS Online with the organization ID and password
- Click **Groups**
- Create New Group
- Add Group Name, Summary, and Tags
- Create privacy settings using the radio buttons and click on **Create Group**.
- Invite members to the group by clicking on **Invite Users**
- Invite the people to access the Collector for ArcGIS map and choose Send Invitation**.**

* If you are the administrator you will have the option to add people to a group without having them accept the invitation.

- People will have to accept an invitation (unless you are the administrator of your organization) and join the group once you click on send invitation.

COLLECTING DATA USING SURVEY 123 FOR ARCGIS

Survey 123 for ArcGIS web is a very simple web-based app that will allow you to quickly create surveys and map the answers to those surveys on ArcGIS Online. Survey 123 also has some powerful built in analytics that will give you and your students the opportunity to analyze the data they collect right within the app. Of course, you can also go to ArcGIS Online and not only enhance and extend the map of the survey answers, but also create a multitude of apps from that map. The possibilities are endless and so very easy in Survey 123 web. For an example of an activity where students survey trees on their school campus and map that data, go to this activity in the online resources for the book.

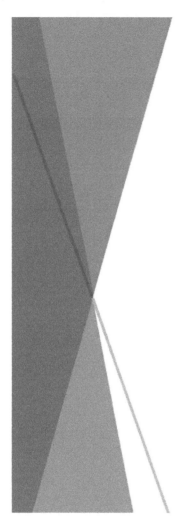

1. OF THE THREE SCENARIOS IN THIS CHAPTER, WHICH ONE HELPED YOU UNDERSTAND DATA CREATION AND ANALYSIS THE MOST?

2. WHICH ONE HELPED YOU THE LEAST? EXPLAIN YOUR RESPONSES IN DETAIL AND HOW IT RELATES TO YOUR CLASSROOM, FUTURE OR PRESENT.

3. CREATE SIMPLE POINT DATA SET BASED ON LATITUDE AND LONGITUDE OR ADDRESSES. BE MINDFUL OF THE ATTRIBUTES YOU WANT TO COLLECT FOR EACH RECORD. ADD THE DATA TO A MAP, SAVE IT, AND SHARE IT.

CHAPTER 6: THE GIS ADVANTAGE - ANALYSIS

Making GIS maps is exciting. Seeing the data come alive is even more exciting. The most empowering aspect of ArcGIS Online maps is the deeply detailed, "live" datasets behind each layer of points, lines, and polygons. ArcGIS Online has the capability to create customized symbols and analyze the data to quickly see patterns and draw conclusions. Teachers and students can make "on the fly" changes that better reflect and address the topic, skill, or question that is being taught.

Let's examine this by looking at a free pre-created map that visualizes the American Civil War, http://arcg.is/2qC6AmC. With this one map, you can:

- Show all battles and states as one country and one war, or the states can quickly be symbolized and categorized based on allegiance and the battles can be classified based on the victor. These two techniques are simple ways to shift the geographic and chronologic scale of the map to accompany the teaching of various stages or perspectives of the Civil War.
- Choosing to "filter" the map to show only the battles in 1861 to focus on the early battles of the conflict.
- Add Map Notes to hyperlink to and incorporate primary source analysis within the same map.
- "Crowdsource" my students' research and opinions by having them add their own placemarks and annotate key people, key events, and key documents using a computer or their smartphone.
- Use ArcGIS Online's advanced analysis tools to conduct simple proximity analysis such as which battles occurred close to capital cities or close to major rivers.

This section will include `several ways to conduct simple and intermediate analysis using ArcGIS Online. This activity is scripted, step-by-step for your introduction to analysis and insure your success.

SIMPLE ANALYSIS AT YOUR FINGER TIPS

Some of the most common and simplest tools to help make your maps interactive and communicative are at your fingertips. ArcGIS Online's most common analytical tools are accessed beneath the title of each layer so that they are easily accessible. Through a series of scenarios, this section provides steps for students to complete simple analysis.

FOLLOW ALONG AS WE EXPLORE ANALYSIS

 YOU ARE TEACHING ABOUT THE CIVIL WAR AND WANT TO JAZZ UP THE TEACHING OF THE WAR BY HAVING YOUR STUDENTS CONDUCT SOME SIMPLE GIS ANALYSIS. YOU DECIDE YOU WILL HAVE YOUR STUDENTS LEARN SOME SIMPLE GIS ANALYSIS TOOLS WHILE ALSO COVERING SOME CONTENT.

- Go to www.arcgis.com and sign in using the ArcGIS Online public or organizational account credentials.
- Choose **Map** and then Choose New Map to create a new map. This will confirm that there is no lingering data from a previous project.

ADD DATA

- Click on Content and then click on Add -> Search for Layers.
- Add the layer G4T_CWStates by searching **in ArcGIS Online.**
- Find: CWStates in ArcGIS Online, and uncheck the Within Map Area box
- Click on the **Add link** to the right of the G4T_CWStates layer that appears and click on Done Adding Layers.

SYMBOLIZE AND RENAME G4T_CW STATES

- Changing symbols is a simple and powerful way to help analyze the data based on differences. These differences can be nominal, ordinal, or quantitative data.

- Click on Content and then click on the layer G4T_CWStates. Then choose the Change Style icon below the layer name.
- Symbolize each state based on the side they fought. To do this change the attribute to CWCOUNTRY. Select a drawing style for the states by clicking on Options.
- Edit the symbols to United States of America- Blue, Confederate States of America - Grey, Border States - Yellow, and Western Territories – Brown.
- Click on the color box to the left of the LABEL. Change the FILL color to a blue color. Click OK.
- Scroll down to Confederate States of America and click on the color box to the left of the LABEL. Change the color to gray. Click OK.
- Scroll down to Border States and click on the color box to the left of the LABEL.
- Change the FILL color to a shade of Yellow. Click OK
- Scroll down to Western Territories and click on the color box to the left of the LABEL.
- Change the FILL color to a shade of Brown. Click OK, OK again, and Click DONE*
  *THIS IS VERY IMPORTANT. If the OK button and DONE is not clicked again the color changes WILL NOT be applied.

RENAME G4T_CWStates

- Click on the layer G4T_CWStates. Then choose the More Options icon below the layer name.
- Choose the option to Rename the layer and change it to Civil War States.
- Click OK

SAVE EARLY & SAVE OFTEN

Like any computer document –it is wise to save your work early and often in ArcGIS Online.

Click on Save and give the map a name, tags, summary and provide a destination to save the project.

ADD & SYMBOLIZE A FEW MORE LAYERS

- Click on Content and then click on Add -> Search for Layers
- Add the layer G4T_CWCapitals by searching in ArcGIS Online and NOT within the map area.
- Click Done Adding Layers
- Click on the G4T_CWCapitals layer name and choose Change Style. Choose the option Show Location Only
- Click Option, Symbols, Shapes, and choose an orange star (make the size 24).
- Click OK, Click OK again, and Click DONE
- Rename the layer Capital Cities, and zoom out to view your map.
- Search for and Add G4T_Major_Rivers and G4T_Major_Lakes and symbolize them to a shade of blue.
- Rename the layers Major Rivers and Major Lakes
- Click on SAVE to save your work.

ADD & SYMBOLIZE G4T_CWBattles

- Click on Content and then click on Add -> Search for Layers
- Add the layer G4T_CWBattles by searching in ArcGIS Online and NOT within the map area.
  - Click on the G4T_CWBattles layer name and choose Change Style.
  - Choose an attribute to show Victor
  - Select a drawing style -> Types (Unique Symbols)-> Choose Options.
  - Click on each symbol next to each LABEL and assign the following colors:

- o USA -> Dark Blue
- o CSA -> Dark Gray
- o INC -> Beige

- Rename the layer All Battles

SHARE THE MAP

- Click on Share and then click on a classroom group or everyone. Close the window.
- Click on Save to save the map.
- Nice Going!! A simple interactive Civil War Map has been created that we will now use to learn how to take advantage of the Show Table and Filter Tools.

SHOW TABLE & FILTER

The remaining analysis tools that are simple and powerful are the **Show Table** and **Filter** tools.

Show Table - allows interaction with the data table and attributes connected with the feature class.

Filter - allows selection and will only show features based on one or more attributes. For instance, cities can be filtered by population, Civil War battles by year, etc. To help grasp how these tools work, practice using the Filter and Show Table tools using the Civil War Map just created.

OPEN AND EDIT AN EXISTING PROJECT

Now we will edit the map that we made. Let's visualize and analyze the Civil War for 1861, 1862, 1863, 1864, and 1865. Go to www.arcgis.com and sign in using your credentials. Choose Content and open the Civil War Map that you created during the previous section.

- Click on Home and then click on Gallery-> Search for G4T_CWMap
- Click on the map name link -> Open in Map Viewer

FILTER THE ALL BATTLE LAYER TO JUST SHOW BATTLES, 1861

- Click on Contents
- Make sure All Battles is checked on.
- Filter the All Battles layer so that only battles from 1861 are visible. To do this:
  - Click on the layer name All Battles and click on the Filter icon
  - Set the Filter so that BEGIN_YEAR is 1861
- Click on Apply Filter and Zoom To
- Notice that you just made a map showing only the battles from 1861,

COLLECT STATISTICS ABOUT 1861 BATTLES

- You will now use the Show Table function to find out how many battles and casualties occurred in 1861.
- Click on the layer name All Battles and click on the Show Table icon
- Click on the Field Name TotCas
- Click on the Field Name TotCas and choose Statistics.

- **How many Civil War casualties were there in 1861?**
- Find out which battle had the highest number casualties in 1861 and how many casualties occurred during the battle.
    - Click on the layer name All Battles and click on the Show Table icon
    - Scroll to the right and click on the Field Name TotCas and choose Sort Descending.
- **Which battle had the most casualties in 1861?**

CONTINUE PRACTICING THE FILTER AND STATISTICS TOOL

Repeat the steps for 1861 and analyze the chronology of the Civil War by changing your filter based on the years 1862, 1863, 1864, and 1865. The end goal is ending with a chronological map of the Civil War.

- Hover over the All Battles layer and click on More Options -> Copy
- Notice a copy of the layer shows up at the top of the list of layers.
- Rename the copied layer 1861 Battles

- Hover over the 1861 Battle layer and click on More Options -> Copy.
- Notice a copy of the layer appears at the top of the list of layers.
- Rename the layer, 1862 Battles
- Hover over the layer, 1862 Battles, Choose the Filter icon, and change the filter so that the layer only show BEGIN_YEAR is 1862
- Hover over the 1862 Battles layer and click on More Options -> Copy.
- Notice a copy of the layer appears at the top of the list of layers.
- Rename the layer, 1863 Battles
- Hover over the layer, 1863 Battles, Choose the Filter icon, and change the filter so that the layer only show BEGIN_YEAR is 1863
- Hover over the 1863 Battle layer and click on More Options -> Copy.
- Rename the layer, 1864 Battles
- Hover over the layer, 1864 Battles, choose the Filter icon, and change the filter so that the layer only show BEGIN_YEAR is 1864
- Hover over the 1864 Battles layer and click on More Options -> Copy.
- Rename the layer, 1865 Battles
- Hover over the layer, 1865 Battles, Choose the Filter icon, and change the filter so that the layer only shows BEGIN_YEAR is 1865
- Use the Show Table tool to find out total casualties for each year of the Civil War and to record which battle had the highest number of casualties each year.

This concludes the first taste of using ArcGIS Online simple analysis tools. While this scenario focused on the Civil War, think about the topics you may want to map similarly using the Change Style, Filter, and Show Table tools.

BEYOND THE BASICS: ARCGIS ONLINE'S ORGANIZATIONAL ANALYSIS TOOLS

The previously introduced tools are available with and without an ArcGIS Online Organizational Account. The tools below are some of the most useful and applicable to the classroom. Unless noted, **an ArcGIS Online Organizational Account is necessary to access the tools and to perform the analysis functions**.

It is also wise for you and your students to always click on the "Check Credit" link every time you do an analysis prior to clicking on the Run Analysis button. Most of the time the credits consumed should be a fraction of one credit. With a suggested yearly maximum of 15 credits per student, being aware of how many credits used for an individual activity is essential.

EASY ANALYSIS TOOLS FOR CLASS ACTIVITIES AND PROJECTS

SYMBOLOGY (NO ACCOUNT NEEDED) – ADDING DATA LAYERS AND SYMBOLIZING DATA TO MAKE COMPARISONS OF AREAS.

Examples:

- Comparing World Demographics
- Comparing Election Results/Public Opinion

- Comparing Energy Consumption
- Comparing Pollution levels
- Comparing Earthquake intensity

To change the symbology of a layer:

- Click on or Hover over the layer to re-symbolize
- Click on Change Style
- Change the symbols and colors

FILTERING (QUERYING) – FILTERING DATA BASED ON ATTRIBUTE VALUES. USEFUL FOR TEACHING HOW TO LOOK AT SUBSETS OF DATA, OR HOW TO CREATE DATA FROM DATA WHEN FILTERING BASED ON MULTIPLE ATTRIBUTES.

Examples – Querying the Reach of Jim Crow, Querying and comparing River Systems, Querying Civil War Battles, Querying public survey results, High Schools, Middle Schools, or Elementary Schools, selecting a range of values.

To Filter data in a layer:

- Click on or hover over the layer to filter
- Click on Filter
- Set the filter parameters

CREATE BUFFERS OR DRIVE TIME AREAS

The Buffer tool creates areas around point, line, or area features to a specified distance. You can create single ring and multi-ring buffers.

The Drive Time Areas tool creates areas that can be reached within a specified travel time based on a mode of travel.

Examples:

- New Mexico does not allow alcohol to be sold within 300 feet of an active school, church, or military installation. Use the buffer tool to create restriction areas.
- A researcher wants to know how many citizens live within a certain distance to Walmarts, Superfund sites, the Mississippi River system, etc.
- Someone is mapping setback requirements to know whether they can build a structure based on local building codes
- A delivery restaurant wants to know how many patrons live within 4, 8, and 12 minutes of their facility.
- A school division wants to know how many of the division students live within 30 minutes of their high school.

To access the Create Buffers or Drive Time Areas tool:

- Click on or hover over the layer that contains the data on which the Buffer or Drive Time Areas will be based
- Click on Perform Analysis -> Proximity Analysis
- Choose Create Buffers or Drive Time Areas
- Remember to click on Show Credit link to see proposed credit consumption

JOIN FEATURES TOOL WILL TRANSFER ATTRIBUTES FROM ONE LAYER OR TABLE TO ANOTHER BASED ON SPATIAL AND ATTRIBUTE RELATIONSHIPS. OPTIONALLY, STATISTICS CAN BE CALCULATED FOR THE JOINED FEATURES.

Examples:

- Crime Analysis – crimes joined to school districts, zip codes, streets
- Accidents – joined by road segments, mile post markers, etc
- Businesses – households joined to closest store
- Litter – pieces of trash joined to closest trash can

To access the Join Features tool:

- Click on or hover over the layer that contains the point data to join to another layer
- Click on Perform Analysis -> Summarize Data
- Choose the Join Features Tool
- Remember to click on Show Credit link to see proposed credit consumption

SUMMARIZE WITHIN TOOL CALCULATES STATISTICS IN AREAS WHERE AN INPUT LAYER OVERLAPS A BOUNDARY LAYER.

Examples:

- How many miles of the Mississippi River system flow within each state? Each county?
- How many miles of the Appalachian Trail intersect each state or county?

- A cable provider is starting a pilot program where it provides low-cost Internet access to low-income community college students. Summarize Within can be used to determine the number of low-income families in each college district so the cable provider can choose an appropriate district for its pilot program.
- How many Walmarts are in each state?
- How many Civil War Battles happened in each state?

To access the Summarize Within tool

- Click on or hover over the layer that contains the data to summarize
- Click on Analysis -> Summarize Data
- Choose the Summarize Within tool
- Remember to click on Show Credit link to see proposed credit consumption

FIND EXISTING LOCATIONS IS USED TO CREATE NEW FEATURES BASED ON ONE OR MORE ATTRIBUTE OR SPATIAL QUERIES, LIKE SELECTION BY ATTRIBUTE AND SELECTION BY LOCATION IN ARCGIS.

Examples:

- I want to know areas that are zoned for recreation and school
- I want to know how many counties are named after Jefferson and Adams
- I want to know the counties with a population greater than 100,000 people that are in Georgia.

To access the Find Existing Locations tool

- Click on or hover over the layer that contains the data to analyze and derive existing locations from
- Click on Analysis -> Find Locations
- Choose the Derive Existing Locations tool
- Remember to click on Show Credit link to see proposed credit consumption

INTERPOLATE IS METHOD OF CONSTRUCTING NEW DATA POINTS WITHIN THE RANGE OF A DISCRETE SET OF KNOWN DATA POINTS.

Examples:

- I want to interpolate the temperature between cities in my state or county.
- I want to interpolate the cell phone signal around my school's campus
- I want to interpolate Wi-Fi coverage in my school
- I want to interpolate snowfall from the last storm based on data collected by students all over campus.
- I want to create an interpolated map based on elevation points.

To access the Interpolate tool:

- Click on or hover over the layer that contains the point data to interpolate
- Click on Analysis -> Analyze Patterns
- Choose the Interpolate tool
- Remember to click on Show Credit link to see proposed credit consumption

DENSITY IS USED TO CALCULATE AND VISUALIZE DENSITY OF AN AREA BASED ON POINT OR LINE DATA.

Examples:

- Density of crimes or traffic accidents
- Density of trash on campus or in your community
- Density of wildlife observations

To access the Density tool:

- Click on or hover over the layer containing the point data upon which the density analysis is based
- Click on Analysis -> Analyze Patterns
- Choose the Calculate Density Tool
- Remember to click on Show Credit link to see proposed credit consumption

To help gain experience using these tools here are some real-world classroom examples in which students have used the tools to help support their learning.

 FOLLOW ALONG AS WE EXPLORE ANALYSIS

ANALYSIS SCENARIO 1

 Your students are doing a research project on commerce in your areas. They decide to look at Walmart because they located a layer in ArcGIS Online. They can use this file to do some analysis to answer their guiding questions and visualize their research.

GUIDING QUESTIONS - HOW MANY WALMARTS ARE THERE IN EACH COUNTY IN VIRGINIA? HOW MUCH OF VIRGINIA IS WITHIN 25 AND 50 MILES OF A WALMART?

LAYERS NEEDED

- Point layer showing the locations of Walmarts in Virginia
- Area (polygon) layer showing the counties in Virginia

SUMMARIZE WITHIN - STEPS TO COUNT THE NUMBER OF WALMARTS IN EACH COUNTY OF VIRGINIA THAT CAN BE USED TO CREATE A THEMATIC MAP.

- Sign into ArcGIS Online and open this web map, https://arcg.is/1L0efK.
- Click on Analysis button
- Choose Summarize Data -> Summarize Within
- Set up Layer Relationships
    - Make VaCounties the layer to summarize other features within its boundaries
    - Make Va_Walmarts the layer to summarize
    - Leave as Count of Points
    - Leave as Field
    - Change the Name to "G4T_SummarizeINITIALS"
- Remember to click on Show Credit link to see proposed credit consumption
- Choose Run

STYLE

- On the newly created layer, change Style to Counts/Amounts->Options->Classify Data->Quantile-> 5 classes
- Click OK -> Done.

MULTI-RING BUFFER - STEPS TO CREATE A MULTI RING BUFFER TO VISUALIZE HOW MUCH OF VIRGINIA IS WITHIN IN 25 AND 50 MILES OF A WALMART.

- Click on the Analysis button
- Choose Use Proximity->Create Buffers-> VA_Walmarts->Size to 25 50 Miles (note the space between each value is to create a multi-ring buffer)
- Click Options and Choose Dissolve
- Change Name to G4T_WalmartMultiBuffferINITIALS
- Remember to click on Show Credit link to see proposed credit consumption.

- Zoom in and out to different areas of Virginia to see the reach of Walmart. Also click on Show Table to see the statistics and how much of Virginia is within 25 and 50 miles of a Walmart.
- Create screen captures of each of the layers created and include in a presentation (teacher or student)

ANALYSIS SCENARIO 2

 A group of students are doing a project on Traffic Accidents in Albemarle County (VA) and Charlottesville (VA). They are interested in finding out where the accidents are occurring and if certain roads or sections of roads are more dangerous than others.

GUIDING QUESTIONS: WHICH AREAS OF ALBEMARLE COUNTY AND CHARLOTTESVILLE EXPERIENCED THE HIGHEST DENSITY OF TRAFFIC ACCIDENTS IN T 2015? WHICH SECTIONS OF MAJOR ROADS IN ALBEMARLE COUNTY AND CHARLOTTESVILLE CITY EXPERIENCED THE HIGHEST NUMBER OF FATAL ACCIDENTS IN 2015?

LAYERS NEEDED

- Point layer showing the location of accidents in Albemarle County and Charlottesville City. This data is courtesy of the Virginia Department of Transportation.

- Line layer showing the major roads in Albemarle County. This data set was obtained by doing a search in ArcGIS Online for the Average Annual Daily Traffic in Virginia. The data is courtesy of the Virginia Department of Transportation.
- Area (polygon) layer showing the county and city boundaries of Virginia. This data set is courtesy of Esri's Maps and Data.

MAP SET UP

- Sign into ArcGIS Online and open map - https://arcg.is/0LWSm5
- Click on the Modify Map button and then click on Content
- Turn on the G4T AlbCoAccidents Density layer.
- Filter the Counties layer so that only Fatal crashes are visible. To show how the density of all accidents compare to just fatalities, you will filter the Counties layer so that only Fatal crashes are visible. This is necessary to set the area to control/clip the extent of the density analysis
- To do this click on the layer G4T AlbCoAccidents and choose the Filter tool.
  - Create an expression: CRASH_TYPE is Fatal Crash
- Choose Apply Filter and Zoom To

DENSITY - HOW TO CALCULATE DENSITY OF CAR ACCIDENTS IN CHARLOTTESVILLE AND ALBEMARLE COUNTY

- Click on the Analysis Button
- Click on Analyze Patterns->Calculate Density
- Make the layer you just filtered for fatal crashes only G4T_AlbCoAccidents the layer to calculate density
- No count field is needed for this analysis;

- Click on Options; Set the search radius to 2 miles
- Clip Output to Drawn Borders
- Classify by Natural Breaks
- Number of Classes to 8
- Name the layer G4T_AlbCoFatalities Density (initials)
- Remember to click on Show Credit link to see proposed credit consumption
- Choose Run

ANALYZE THE RESULTS

- Click on More Options for the G4T AlbCoFatalities Density layer.
- Click on Transparency slider and adjust back and forth to see the comparison between the fatalities and all accidents in 2015.

*NOTE – PERFORMING ANALYSIS ON MANY RECORDS CAN ADD UP AND USE MANY CREDITS. ALWAYS CLICK ON SHOW CREDITS LINK TO SEE HOW MANY CREDITS WILL BE USED WHEN RUNNING AN ANALYSIS. SOMETIMES IT MAY BE BEST TO RUN THE ANALYSIS ONCE, AND THEN SHARE THE LAYER WITH THE STUDENTS.

What statements can you make regarding the connections between the density of fatalities and the density of all accidents in that year? Think about the number of dots in each of the density layers? Does that have a connection to the results you are seeing?

Collectively this analysis provides a new understanding of traffic accidents at the local level. Analysis often spawns further questions, such as: Which areas are prone to accidents? Where should EMS centers be located? Where should police officers patrol? Should speed limits be decreased in certain areas?

TEACHING IDEA

HAVE STUDENTS WRITE A SHORT PARAGRAPH ABOUT THE SPATIAL PATTERNS OF ACCIDENTS IN ALBEMARLE COUNTY BASED ON EACH TYPE ANALYSIS (DENSITY, SPATIAL JOIN, SHOW TABLE/SORT DESCENDING).

ANALYSIS SCENARIO 3

A group of students are doing a project on the major river systems of the United States and were assigned the Mississippi River System. They would like to create a map that shows the Mississippi River, the major rivers of the Mississippi River System, and all the US States that intersect these rivers.

LAYERS NEEDED:

- **Major Rivers of the US** – Line layer that contains the major rivers of the United States that contains the following attributes: NAME, SYSTEM
- **US States** – Area (polygon) that contains the US States.

MAP SET-UP

1. Log into ArcGIS Online.
2. Click on Map -> Add-> Search for Layers
3. Find and Add G4T_Ch6Sc3 in ArcGIS Online and make sure Within Map Area is not selected.
4. Save the map at G4T_Mississippi_SystemINITIALS and set the sharing parameters as Private, Organization, or Public.

Use Find Existing Locations to create three new layers: The Mississippi River, The Mississippi River System, and States that Intersect the Mississippi River System.

CREATE A LAYER THAT JUST CONTAINS THE MISSISSIPPI RIVER

1. Click on G4T_Major Rivers -> Click Analysis
2. Click on Find Locations -> Find Existing Locations

3. Click on Add Expression
4. In the Add Expression window create an expression that reads:

> **G4T_Major_Rivers <Where (attribute query>**
>
> **NAME is Mississippi**

5. Click Add and then name the result layer G4T_MissR_INITIALS
6. Remember to click on Show Credit link to see proposed credit consumption
7. Click on Run Analysis
8. Rename G4T_MissR_INITIALS to Mississippi River

CREATE A LAYER THAT JUST CONTAINS RIVERS THAT ARE PART OF THE MISSISSIPPI RIVER

1. Click on G4T_Major Rivers -> Click Analysis
2. Click on Find Locations -> Find Existing Locations
3. Choose layer to be Major Rivers
4. Click on Add Expression
5. In the Add Expression window create an expression that reads:

> **G4T_Major_Rivers <Where (attribute query>**
>
> **SYSTEM is Mississippi**

6. Name the result layer G4T_MissSystem_INITIALS
7. Remember to click on Show Credit link to see proposed credit consumption
8. Click on Run Analysis
9. Rename G4T_MissSystem_INITIALS to Mississippi River System

CREATE A LAYER THAT JUST CONTAINS ALL THE US STATES THAT INTERSECT A MAJOR RIVER THAT IS PART OF THE MISSISSIPPI RIVER SYSTEM.

1. Click on G4T_States_General -> Click Analysis
2. Click on Find Locations -> Find Existing Locations
3. Choose layer to be states general
4. Click on Add Expression
5. In the Add Expression window create an expression that reads:

G4T_States_General <intersects>

Mississippi River System

---

6. Name the result layer G4T_MissStates_INITIALS
7. Remember to click on Show Credit link to see proposed credit consumption
8. Click on Run Analysis
9. Rename G4T_MissStates_INITIALS to Mississippi River System

PREPARE FINAL MAP FOR DISPLAY

- Remove the layer G4T_States_General
- Make sure the layers are in the following draw-order and Change the Style for the layers so that:
- Mississippi River – Red
- Mississippi River System – Red
- G4T_Major Rivers – Blue
- Mississippi River States - Beige
- Turn of the Mississippi River, Mississippi River System, and Mississippi River States layers.
- Save and Share your Map

Students or a teacher could now use this map to help students visualize and understand the following questions:

- *What is the Mississippi River? (turn on Mississippi River)*
- *What is the Mississippi River System? (Turn on the Mississippi River System)*
- *Which States are part of the Mississippi River System? (Turn on the Mississippi River States)*

ANALYSIS SCENARIO 4

A group of students are in science class researching seasonal temperatures and would like to create maps that show how temperatures in the United States differ in January, April, July, and October. They decide they will create four simple interpolated temperature maps showing the average temperatures during these months for the United States based on NOAA data collected between 1981 - 2010.

LAYERS NEEDED

- A point layer with temperature data for 1981 - 2010 for major cities in the US.
- A polygon (area) layer for the continental United States

SET UP THE MAP FOR ANALYSIS

- Sign into ArcGIS Online and click on Map
- Go to http://arcg.is/2iQKtW8 and download the .csv file to the computer.
- Add the G4T data to your ArcGIS Online map. To do this:
  - Click on Add ->Add Layer from File-> Choose File
  - Navigate to the downloaded file, G4T_NOAA_AvgTemp -> Import Layer
  - Locate the layer using Address
  - Make sure the country is the United States
  - Choose Add Layer
  - Click on Done to exit the smart mapping interface.
- Search for add the G4T_States layer. To do this:
  - Click on Add->Search for Layers in ArcGIS Online and make sure within map area is not selected (checked)

- o   Find G4T_States
- o   Choose Add
- o   Click Done Adding Layers
- Move the G4T Temperature above the G4T_States

INTERPOLATE THE G4T_TEMPERATURE LAYER. TO DO THIS:

- Hover over G4T_Temperature and click on Analysis
  - o   Choose Analyze Patterns -> Interpolate Points
  - o   Make sure the point layer is G4T_NOAA_AvgTemp
  - o   Set the field to interpolate to be Avg_Jan
  - o   Choose Options -> Click Output to G4T_States
    - Classify by Geometric Interval using 10 classes
  - o   Name the layer G4T_JanTempINITIALS
  - o   Remember to click on Show Credit link to see proposed credit consumption
  - o   Choose Run Analysis

SYMBOLIZE THE G4T_INTERPOLATION LAYER.

- Click on G4T_JanTempINITIALS -> Change Style
  - o   Select Value Max as the attribute to show
  - o   Select Counts and Amounts (Color) ->Options
    - Click on Classify Data ->5 Classes
    - Choose Round Classes -> 10
    - Choose OK then Done

Repeat the steps above to create interpolated temperature maps for April (Avg_Apr), July (Avg_July), and October (Avg_Oct). Save each file as: G4T_AprilTempINITIALS; G4TJulyTempINITIALS, and G4TOctTempsINITIALS

SHARE THE MAP WITH THE BASIC MAP APP

Once the analysis is completed, create a Basic Map Viewer that could be shared with others or embedded into a website or presentation.

FIRST - Save the Map.

- Click on Save
- Title: G4T_TempAnalysisINITIALS
- Tags: G4T, Interpolation
- Description: Average Temperatures in the Continental US based on data collected by NOAA between 1981 - 2010.
- Save in Folder: Save in a folder in your ArcGIS account that will be easy to identify and locate.
- Click on Save Map

SECOND - Share the Map with the Basic Viewer App

The Basic Viewer App allows sharing the contents of their map with some interactivity and limited, customized access to your data and layers.

- Click on Share
- Decide how to share it (Public, Your Organization, a Group or keep it Private)
- If prompted, update the sharing properties for the layers in the map.
- To share the finished map, use the link provided.
- Click on Create a Web App ->Configurable Apps
- Select Basic Viewer -> Create Web App
- Configure the settings for the Web App
    - General - reconfigure the general settings for the web app as needed.
    - Theme - reconfigure the color themes and layout options as needed
    - Options - decide which tools and options you'd like people to have access to.
    - Search - enable or disable the option to search for locations.

Click on Save. Click on the Share link the Basic Viewer Map window to get the link to share with people.

TEACHING IDEA

HAVE STUDENTS ANALYZE PATTERNS ON THE MAP. HAVE THEM CLICK ON CERTAIN CITIES IN COASTAL AND INTERIOR AREAS TO CALCULATE THE RANGE OF AVERAGE LOW AND HIGH TEMPERATURES DURING DIFFERENT MONTHS. WHICH AREAS APPEAR TO EXPERIENCE THE LARGEST DIFFERENCES IN LOW AND HIGH TEMPERATURES? WHY DO YOU THINK THIS IS THE CASE?

SEE AN EXAMPLE FOR A TRADITIONAL CLASSROOM SETTING THAT USES GIS ANALYSIS TO FIGURE OUT THE BEST DECISION FOR INSTALLING A RAILWAY FROM ST. LOUIS. **SEE ONLINE APPENDIX D AND E** FOR THE ACTIVITY AND HANDOUTS.

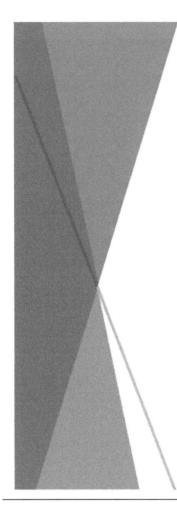

REVIEW THE ANALYSIS TOOLS IN THIS CHAPTER. WHICH ANALYSIS TOOL RESONATES WITH YOU?

WHAT ABOUT THAT ANALYSIS TOOL WAS MOST COMPELLING?

HOW WILL YOU RELATE THAT TO WHAT YOU TEACH?

GOLD STANDARD PBL & THE GEOINQUIRY PROCESS

According to the Buck Institute (http://www.bie.org), "Project Based Learning is a teaching method in which students gain knowledge and skills by working for an extended period to investigate and respond to an authentic, engaging, and complex question, problem, or challenge." For more information on PBL basics, go to Buck Institute's PBL YouTube channel at http://bit.ly/PBLVideos.

This type of teaching can often be confused with teaching a unit and having a project at the end of the unit. The difference between the two is in the ongoing nature of the project in a PBL. When the project is introduced at the beginning of the unit, the lessons are geared towards helping students add to the project throughout the unit, rather than just at the end. Students are asked to reflect on what they've learned and how it adds to the project on which they're working. Students are asked to critique and to receive critiques from fellow students and make revisions based on those critiques. PBLs can be a powerful teaching method.

The essential elements of a gold standard PBL are:

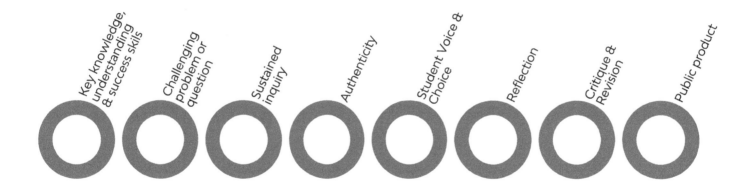

- **Key Knowledge, Understanding, and Success Skills**: These are at the heart of your PBL. Teachers must know what they want to the students to know, understand, and be able to do at the end of the project. Key knowledge is the standards around which you are building your PBL. Understanding encompasses why the standards are relevant. Think of the skills you'd want an ideal graduate to have: the ability to collaborate, to solve problems, to think critically, the ability to plan, to reflect, to make changes. These are your success skills. Which success skills are easily embedded with your project?
- **Challenging Problem or Question**: The question should be specific, kid-friendly, and open-ended. It might also include a role you want students to take - park ranger, hydrologist, meteorologist, geologist, geographer, researcher, etc. There shouldn't be a single answer to a driving question. It should encourage students to ask more questions.
- **Sustained Inquiry**: Your project should offer students the chance to ask questions, answer them, and during more study, ask additional questions. It might require helping students determine whether their new questions align to your learning goal, but the ability of students to ask and answer questions of their own choosing is a powerful pedArcGIS Onlinegical tool.
- **Authenticity**: Does your project matter to your students? Ask students to determine cell phone coverage around town, to determine how far you'd have to drive to find the two distinct types of Girl Scout cookie bakeries, to tell a story that is personal to the student, have students plan a trip itinerary, complete with mileage, travel times, and cost. Find ways of modifying what you're already doing to make it more authentic to your audience.
- **Student Voice and Choice**: This is exactly what it sounds like. It is both the easiest and hardest part of PBL. Giving students a voice and choice on what and how they learn is important. Being able to give up the ability to control what happens in your classroom and to know what is coming next is really challenging. Give students options within a project that allows them to learn what you need them to learn but with the ability to put their own stamp on their learning.
- **Reflection**: A vital part of a gold-standard PBL. Students must engage in reflection on what they've learned, how they've learned, and what they still need to know. This is an effective way for students to

reflect on the success skills you've chosen for your PBL. A reflection question could be as simple as, "How did I make a positive impact on my team today?" or "What do I need from my teammates to be more successful tomorrow.?" Reflection questions can be a quick and easy exit ticket that gives the teacher insight on where students need to start the next day.

- **Critique and Revision**: Students are used to receiving feedback from teachers. When that feedback comes with a number attached, students are far more likely to focus on the grade rather than the qualitative feedback included. In this instance, critique is not about a grade, it's about improving a student's work. More importantly, the critique should come from fellow students as much as, if not more, than the teacher. This requires some teaching of how to give and receive constructive criticism, but it's a vital part of the process. In addition, students must be taught how to act on the critique to revise. This is as much about critical thinking as anything else. Sometimes a critique helps you focus on something you missed. Sometimes a critique shows a misunderstanding of your topic and can be put aside. Students need to know how to deal with both types.
- **Public Product**: Students will often approach projects that have a public product in a very different way than they will projects they know are destined for their teacher's eyes only. Give students a chance to share what they've learned with a wider audience: a presentation at school to parents, experts in the field, to other students. Allow students to publish their work as a web page or other medium open to the share with the public.

Together, these eight pieces create a gold standard PBL. Gold standard PBLs are great for students and teachers, but let's face the reality of teaching: Teachers don't always have time for a gold-standard PBL. Sometimes we have time to weave only one or two elements into a unit. This is the time for teacher reflection: When a unit is finished, with the one or two PBL elements, make some notes about adjustments needed for next year. What one or two additional PBL elements will get added? What worked, what didn't? Ask the students for their feedback. The feedback can sometimes be a little more honest than preferred, but it gives a point from which to adjust. Don't get caught up in the trap of all or nothing. Start small and build from there.

GIS weaves easily into the PBL framework. If students are asked to solve a problem with GIS, that begs for a driving question. "How can we, as meteorologists, ensure that there are enough tornado sirens located with a given area?" If students are expected to tell a story using a story map, with the switch of a toggle, you have a public product. Give students questions to answer: How can GIS help solve a problem? How can GIS be used to analyze data? By letting them decide what problem or what data to analyze, students are given choice and a voice.

Always start with key knowledge, understanding, and success skills. When planning any unit of instruction, always start with what students should know, understand, and be able do at the end of the unit. Take the time to list all the things to accomplish with the unit, then decide another essential element that should be included. Be sure to include those success skills - problem solving, collaboration, critical thinking - on the list to ensure that those skills are being taught throughout the unit.

The key criteria for the **Geographic Inquiry Process** include:

- Ask Geographic Questions
- Acquire Geographic Resources
- Explore Geographic Data
- Analyze Geographic Information
- Act on Geographic Knowledge

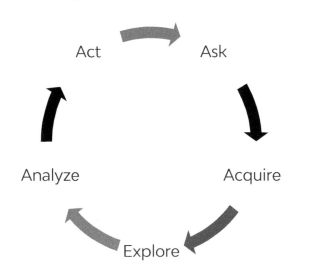

The Geographic Inquiry Process (Esri, 2003) is the recommended framework used to facilitate PBL GIS. The process tasks students with identifying a geographic question and then following the inquiry process to draw conclusions or take action. The key criteria for the Geographic Inquiry Process include:

Ask Geographic Questions

The foundation of a solid GIS project is the question and secondary questions that students will ask. Initially, several students may struggle making the question geographic. Students struggle, feeling that they must ask complex and original questions. The key is to encourage simple and targeted questions. The complex questions often reveal themselves during the process. As they work through the simpler questions students may need to revise their questions or add more questions that they will have to answer. This is all part of the process and requires both the teacher and the student to be flexible.

Some examples of geographic questions

Location Questions:

- Where are most accidents occurring? Why there?
- Where are accidents not occurring? Why Not?
- Where should a new high school be built?
- Where is the wi-fi signal strongest in the school? Weakest?

Relationship Questions:

- What factors are contributing to accidents occurring there?
- What is the relationship between battles and major waterways? Coastal Cities?
- How many people live within 20 minutes of their high school?
- If a bridge is closed, how should the cars be re-routed?
- How should schools be redistricted to maintain optimal demographics?

Temporal Questions

- How has land use changed over time? Which areas have become more urbanized?
- How has the extent of stink bugs in the US changed since 2010?
- How have the location of earthquakes changed since 2000?

Acquire Geographic Resources

Once students have identified the question or set of questions they need to answer it's time to acquire the data they'll need to help answer the question. Many times, acquiring the GIS data will be the lion's share of the time and effort needed for a GIS project.

First, it is important to identify the data they will need to answer their questions. Once the data needs are known they will need to acquire the data.

Common ways to acquire GIS data:

- **Search for layers on ArcGIS Online** (ARCGIS ONLINE) has hundreds of thousands of searchable layers that students can add to their map. It is great for obtaining major roads, waterways, political boundaries, and city locations. It is also a good first place that to point students when they are working on a topic that requires existing data/locations. For instance, a student researched the migration patterns of monarch butterflies. He did a quick search for monarch butterflies and found that a reputable organization had recently published a data set showing the location of butterfly sightings.

- **Search for GIS data using an online search engine.** You can add .shp files and .csv files easily in ArcGIS Online. They key is to use the phrase "GIS data" in your search. For instance, a student was looking for airport locations. To find the data, they simply did a google search for "US airports GIS shapefile" and multiple files popped up.

- **Create the data** – Often your students will have a question that the data exists; however, it is not in a GIS or .csv format. For instance, a student was analyzing the location of car charging stations in Virginia. She found a website that contained a list of charging stations by address. Working with a partner, they created a .csv file containing the name of the station, address, and price per charge. They then added the layer to ARCGIS ONLINE.

- **Collect the data** – For many community and school projects students will need to collect the data. They can use a Geoform, a Google form, Survey 123, an Editable Feature Service, ArcGIS Online Collector App, a GPS unit, or paper and pencil. For instance, a student was researching the location of trash on campus. To make the process simple, she went around campus with a paper map and marked the trash on the map. She then came back to the GIS class and plotted the trash using an Editable Feature Service.

 **Explore Geographic Data**

The next step is to gain a better sense of the data features by making a map and symbolizing the data.

 **Analyze Geographic Information**

After the map is made it is time to analyze the data and help make inferences, draw conclusions, and make decisions. A typical process for analyzing geographic information in the classroom would be:

Look for patterns – once the data is displayed make observations regarding the patterns seen in the data.

- Where are events, incidents, or phenomena occurring?
- Where are events, incidents, or phenomena not occurring?
- What type of spatial pattern is observed? Is the pattern linear? Clustered? Dispersed? Isolated?

Explore the attributes within the patterns observed – use the identify tool to click on map features and explore what attributes may be influencing the observed patterns. For example, if analyzing instances of opioid cases at the US county data level, consider the following attributes:

- Median income
- Unemployment
- Industry
- Age

- Gender
- Rural or Urban

Use the Sort Ascending/Sort Descending tool – this is an easy and powerful tool. Which locations have the highest and lowest rates of a phenomena?

For instance, when studying the distribution of state-level Jim Crows laws in the US between 1865 – 1964 the student may sort types of laws from highest to lowest to identify which states were more concerned and less concerned with marriage, education, public accommodations, and voting participation.

- Conduct GIS Analysis - Choose the right tools to analyze the data based on the questions you are exploring and the patterns you observe. Which analysis you use will depend on the topic and questions being answered. Common tools* include:

    - **Filter** – use the filter tool to filter out data sets based on its attributes.
    - **Change Style** – symbolize data using graduated symbols or the heat map technique based on data attributes to look for different patterns. These attributes may be quantitative, qualitative, or temporal.
    - **Find Existing Locations** – use this tool find relationships between layers and locations and to narrow your study area or find out the proportion of instances that coincide with your question.
    - **Summarize Within** – use the Summarize Within tool to count or calculate attribute statistics for events that occur within an area (county, census tract, census block, school classroom, etc).
    - **Join Features** – use the Join Features tool to assign the attributes of an event to another event based on a spatial relationship such as intersection or within a specific distance.
    - **Density** – use this tool to calculate the density of point data

- Interpolation – use this tool to predict unknown values for geographic point data such as Wi-Fi signals, cell phone reception, noise levels, elevation, chemical concentrations, or temperatures.

Specific steps and scenarios to practice using these analysis tools are provided in Chapter 6.

**A note about interpolation – Many times students will incorrectly choose to use the interpolation tool because visually it is more interesting than density. Make sure the interpolation tool is used for point data that is consistent across space such as cell phone reception, noise levels, elevation, temperature, etc. For instance, on several occasions my students have chosen to use interpolate to show where the highest number of accidents are occurring because it looks better than a density analysis (When asked, "Why did you choose this analysis?" Students answered, "It just looked better.") Just because a location is 2 blocks away from an area that experiences a lot of traffic accidents, it doesn't mean there will be more accidents there. The density and join feature tools are much more appropriate for this type of data analysis.*

Act on Geographic Knowledge

Once the analysis is complete, it is time to act on the results and generate a presentation that contextualizes and summarizes the results. The results can be presented as a collection of maps and included in a presentation or delivered as part of a Story Map.

Take Advantage of the Process

It will not always possible to facilitate a full-fledged Geographic Inquiry project, and it is encouraged to regularly leverage pieces of the framework to facilitate inquiry to foster problem solving skills and concepts. Many times, due to time constraints, it will be necessary to craft an activity that provides the students with the question, the data, and the initial map. Students then utilize GIS to analyze and present their conclusions. This is perfectly fine. Doing this is still better than doing nothing. They key is modeling best practice inquiry and incorporating components of the process as much as possible.

REPORT FROM THE FIELD: ELEMENTARY PBL GIS

By Christine Esposito, Johnson Elementary School

WHAT DO YOU TEACH AND WHERE DO YOU TEACH?

I am a gifted specialist at Johnson Elementary, which is a K-4 Title I school in Charlottesville, VA. While my job is mostly pulling small groups of students out of their regular classrooms to deliver instruction; it is also my responsibility to offer support to classroom teachers to help them meet the needs of the gifted and high ability learners in their classrooms. I've helped first grade teachers use GIS with their whole class and given independent projects to my third and fourth graders.

WHY DO YOU USE GIS TO SUPPORT PBL?

As a former sixth grade teacher, I will admit that the idea of teaching GIS to younger elementary students seemed like a crazy idea at first. I soon realized that not only was it not crazy, it was a terrific way to keep kids engaged and to help them see, even at an early age, the role place plays in their lives. An essential element in a gold standard PBL is student choice and voice. I've found that even in elementary school, technology is almost always a student's preference.

Another key component of PBLs is sustained inquiry. It's been my experience that using GIS is a natural fit with sustained inquiry. As they do the initial research for their maps, students are always asking me a million more questions. They've learned that I'm not going to give them the answers, but I may help them figure out where to find the answers. While sometimes those questions may take us a little off-task, I challenge students to find a way to connect their new questions back to our driving question.

HOW DO YOU USE GIS TO SUPPORT PBL?

For the most part, I use GIS as an option for students when doing a PBL. What I've found is that getting one student excited about GIS is easy. As that student starts to work on the GIS portion of their project, other students start asking questions and then want to join in. This year I had third grade students coming to my room during recess to work on their maps.

As an option, GIS is great for a PBL in elementary school. A GIS map and/or Story Map is easily translated into a public product. Students know that their work will be seen by many and work accordingly. An important part of any PBL, but especially those with a public product, is critique and revision. While we are beginning GIS learners, the critique is mostly from me, I've started handing some of that power to students. Teaching students at the elementary level to give constructive feedback is a process. I start by teaching them a simple strategy called two stars and a question. The two stars represent parts of the project students really liked. They must also explain why they liked it, rather than simply saying, "Hey, I love this map note, you used a great color!" The trickier aspect is the question. Students must ask a specific, kind, and helpful question that they have about the project. Questions might start with, "Have you thought about...." or "If you do _____, then maybe _____." Whether we're using GIS to think about public products or revision, critical thinking is a must. Students must look beyond the basics and think about the why when they're using GIS and making decisions.

WHAT ARE SOME OF YOUR BEST EXAMPLES OF USING GIS TO SUPPORT PBL?

Geography of the United States: Our fourth-grade students learn the geography of the United States. Students who finish early can be assigned a PBL that uses GIS. The driving question is "How can you design a map that would help tourists find the most important place in each state?" It is a simple question and a simple map to build. Classroom teachers compile a list of early finishers. Using our organizational account, I give each of the early finishers their own account. I pull them for a short lesson on how to make maps. In most cases, it doesn't take more than 30 minutes to teach fourth graders the basics of using ArcGIS and adding map notes. The biggest struggle for students is remembering to save their work. This is the kind of assignment to which many layers can be added: Students could be asked to determine a driving route to five of the destinations, compute how long it would take them to travel between tourist sites, how much it would cost to take the trip, etc.

Ancient Civilizations: The driving question: "How can we, as researchers, create a museum to showcase ancient civilizations?" The ancient civilizations we study are based on the third grade Standards of Learning in Virginia: China, Egypt, Greece, Mali, and Rome. Students were tasked with being architects, curators, and archivists. One of their options for their museum exhibit was to create a story map that would give visitors more information about their museum. Students learned how to search for layers, add map notes - including links and pictures, and how to build a story map. As part of building a story map, students were taught how to add video, pictures, and text. They also learned how to use Google's advanced search to find pictures that were in the public domain.

Because it's an option rather than the goal, I could conference with students in small groups or one-on-one to give tutorials on what they needed to know. As part of the process, students signed up for lessons they thought they needed. Sometimes they weren't willing to wait for me while I worked with another group. They learned to poke around, to try, to fail, and to find a new way to accomplish what they were trying to do. In some cases, I'm not ashamed to admit students showed me how to do something I didn't know how to do.

In the case of this PBL, GIS was not an original part of my plan. I showed my students a story map as part of their lesson and one of the students wanted to know if they could learn how to make that map too. I learned that third grade is not too early to have students making their own maps.

Toponyms: This was a very quick PBL done with fourth graders. Their driving question was "What can we learn about a place by researching its name?" I had a list of weird place names - Toad Suck, Spuyten Duyvil, Devil's Bit, and Boring, WA to name a few. Students were asked to research the origins of the name and add the data to a crowdsourced map. The back end of this uses an editable feature service, which is slightly more advanced GIS, but it is very easy for students to add data to this kind of map. They used a map note to write an explanation. As students started to realize that place names have a history, they generated lists of places they wanted to learn about.

WHAT ADVICE WOULD YOU GIVE TO A TEACHER WHO IS CONSIDERING GIS PBL?

Go for it. Start small. Small could be everyone learning how to make a map as a whole group activity or it could be working with a very small number of students to teach them the basics. Once I had a core group of 4-5 students who knew how to access ArcGIS, login, start a map or retrieve a previously saved one, and how to add map notes, I called those students my experts. If a student wanted to give GIS a try, one of my experts was dispatched to show them the basics. If they ran into trouble, they'd ask for my help, but that almost never happened.

Many students are willing to try, to fail, and to try again. Once they realize they can't really break anything using ArcGIS, they're far more willing to try new things, to click on buttons and links without worry. I do tell them, repeatedly, to save often and early. On written directions, at the end of every step, I write SAVE. This gets them in the habit of saving and stops most of the anguish of losing what they were working on.

Don't be afraid to say, "I don't know." If you want to build a culture of learning and trust in a classroom, always be willing to be a learner yourself. They're going to ask questions you can't answer. That's OK. There are resources to help you find out. Many of those resources are accessible to upper elementary students so they can figure out the answer to their question. A good PBL isn't just about the content they're learning, it's also about those success skills - collaboration, critical thinking, problem solving, and communicating using a variety of media. GIS allows your students to do all those things with your help, and eventually, on their own.

As students get older, complex analysis plays a bigger role. There were times I thought I wasn't really "doing" GIS with my elementary students because we weren't using the most powerful aspects of GIS. I hope there will come a time when my students have built enough GIS capacity to crawl out on that ledge, but for now, introducing the simple aspects of interactive mapping has done wonders for getting students to change how they think about maps.

REPORT FROM THE FIELD: MIDDLE SCHOOL PBL

By Andy Dojack, William Monroe Middle School

WHAT DO YOU TEACH AND WHERE DO YOU TEACH?

"How do I make this relevant and engaging," is a familiar refrain from teachers operating in a standards-based classroom. Too often, the pressure to cover every aspect or minute detail of a curriculum strand overwhelms teachers. My own experience as a World Geography teacher made me keenly aware of these feelings. As I entered my ninth year of teaching of World Geography I made a choice to shift away from a traditional teacher-led classroom model toward a student-centered model that focused heavily on Project Based Learning (PBL). A key component of student learning was the utilization of online Geographic Information Systems. While my shift to a student-centered model was just me finally adjusting to current pedagogy; my inclusion of GIS was really a springboard to me becoming a better, more innovative teacher.

Four years later I no longer teach a stand-alone World Geography class. Instead, I teach a dedicated GIS class to sixth, seventh, and eighth grade students. In this class students learn the fundamentals of online GIS. Through activities and projects students develop skills in spatial analysis that enhance their learning in core subject areas.

My school, William Monroe Middle School in Stanardsville, VA, is a relatively small school of around 750 students. Despite its smaller size our school division has set a focus on innovation and technological learning. Teachers in our school work hard to meet class standards through the vehicle of 21st century skills. Learning GIS and incorporating it into their classwork allows students the opportunity to grow their critical thinking and analytical skills.

WHY DO YOU USE GIS TO SUPPORT PBL?

Regardless of whether PBL means Project Based Learning, Problem Based Learning, or Performance Based Learning GIS is a useful arrow in any teacher's quiver. GIS allows for the integration of data and location. No longer are students just focusing on the "why" of a problem. GIS allows for an explanation of the 'where' of a problem. Situations arise for many reasons. Very often, that reason is rooted in location. Geography affects matters located to science, civics, and a whole host of other subjects. GIS presents a visual display of information about specific locations.

This visualization of data helps students analyze the spatial patterns regarding certain phenomena. This analysis is often the impetus for student questions and learning. For example, when students learn about life expectancy they are often presented with a list of countries ranked from highest to lowest life expectancy. This same information, presented on a GIS map with additional layers concerning women's education level, prenatal care, and GDP per capita, gives students a cause for exploration. Ten minutes of time exploring the correlation between these factors and life expectancy is a valuable analytical endeavor.

Put simply, I want to help produce students that are thinkers not just fact repeaters. The spatial analysis and critical thinking skills developed through student use of GIS does just this.

HOW DO YOU USE GIS TO SUPPORT PBL?

GIS is useful for data visualization that leads to spatial analysis. If students are considering some sort of problem, the spatial component of GIS provides them with a lens to solve the problem. The ability to see patterns of where and where not among the data sets is essential to problem solving. In my classes I utilize examples of real situations in which GIS was used to solve a problem. Some of these situations deal with serious issues such as disease outbreaks, voting patterns or crime occurrences, whereas others are more benign such as using a spray chart to position your baseball team's infield or how to defend a distinct basketball player. Regardless of the topic, these situations require location analysis and decision making based on patterns of where and where not.

WHAT ARE SOME OF YOUR BEST EXAMPLES OF USING GIS TO SUPPORT PBL?

Local Business and Marketing Plan:

Students used the enriched data layers available in ArcGIS Online to formulate a business plan for our community. By using available demographic measures (population, age distribution, and male/female ratios) along with spending data (Geographically tagged credit card spending information) about our specific county, students identified what businesses had the greatest market potential. Students then used census block data, local zoning ordinance layers, and available real estate points to settle on a retail location.

Which Cell Phone has the Best Location Services: The Scientific Method and GIS

Students hypothesized which cell phones out of a sampling of ten commonly available models featured the best Geo-Location services. To test their hypothesis students constructed a simple survey through Survey123 for ArcGIS. A handheld GPS unit was used to mark the initial control points. Students then used Survey123 to mark each phone's location at the same point used by the handheld. Once the data was collected Survey123 rendered a map with the locations gathered by each phone. The control (handheld points) were added to this map via a .csv upload. The cell phone collected points were the measured with respect to the control points. Students then presented their data in a table form for each phone and each point.

ArcGIS Online Story Maps: GIS to Support Core Class Learning

A tremendous amount of curriculum material covered in core classes contains some sort of spatial tag or location feature. This is not just exclusive to the realm of social studies. Earthquakes and volcanoes in Earth science class and animal migrations and habitat loss and preservation in biology are all location specific. Geography is central to plot structures and themes in many works of literature. Because of this, it is possible to use GIS to support core content instruction through the story mapping feature found in ArcGIS Online.

Students use ArcGIS Online and Story Maps to interpret and analyze the geographic significance and influence of certain events or occurrences. Working with their core teachers, students in my GIS class design a story map to complement a subject covered in either their science, social studies, or language arts class. Using this model students have produced story maps to explain geographic site and situation, disease migration patterns, distribution of cultural landscape sites, and how habitat destruction affects endangered species.

Blending PBL and GIS into your classroom is a decision you will not regret. GIS is applicable to any core subject taught in school today. I currently work to encourage my colleagues to incorporate GIS into at least one lesson each year. While some have reservations about the perceived difficulty of GIS, there are numerous lessons and activities available online that offer a user friendly, curriculum relevant introduction to GIS. The GeoInquiries series from Esri is a wonderful place to start. The Learn ArcGIS webpage also features many student-directed activities that introduce students to spatial analysis.

Many teachers will undoubtedly see the potential of GIS and dive in with both feet. While great, keep in mind the need to build a progression of skills. It is important to know the initial limits of your students. Begin with ready-made activities that help lay a working foundation of skills that allow for a smooth transition to independent student work. If time permits (I would advise teachers to find the time.), allow students exploration time with the mapping software. Once setting up my students with their accounts, I always give them twenty minutes or so to just explore the map. While they all try to find their house or their grandparent's house, they are learning the basics of the platform. This seems to reduce future incidences of students becoming distracted.

As with all teaching, flexibility is of paramount importance when using web based GIS. There will be days where the software will be glitchy because of connectivity issues. There will be various levels of digital literacy among your students. There may even be colleagues that wonder what in the world GIS is. The key is to remain flexible in your instruction and know that the analysis, programing, and critical thinking skills gained with GIS usage are worth it.

REPORT FROM THE FIELD – USING GIS TO POWER UP HIGH SCHOOL PBL

By Chris Bunin, Albemarle High School, Charlottesville VA

WHAT DO YOU TEACH AND WHERE DO YOU TEACH?

I teach AP Human Geography, GIS, and World History at Albemarle High School (AHS). AHS is a high school located in Charlottesville, Virginia with a student population of about 2000 students. I teach GIS as a stand-alone course that is part of James Madison University's dual-enrollment program, The Geospatial Semester (http://bit.ly/2y0SNWK). The goal of the program is to provide high school juniors and seniors with opportunities to participate in inquiry-based learning and have multiple opportunities to use GIS to solve real-world problems.

In addition to the stand-alone GIS course I have introduced my colleagues to way they can use GIS to enhance their social studies and science classes as an analysis tool and presentation tool.

WHY DO YOU USE GIS TO SUPPORT PBL?

The students I teach will be entering college or the workforce within 3 years of taking my classes. Additionally, there is a real push across the state of Virginia to develop real world and authentic performance based activities and assessments. GIS is the most versatile technology I have in my toolbox. With GIS, I can easily integrate:

- Principles of data creation and collection
- Simple and Powerful spatial analytics (filtering, symbology, density, and interpolation)
- Professional quality presentations by making maps or Story Maps.

This, in turn allows me to:

- Introduce my students to a cool technology that connects to their digital lives.
- Seamlessly integrate STEM skills into my non-STEM courses and better reach my more scientifically minded students.
- Prepare my students for the world they will live in. Any student that leaves high school knowing some GIS has an advantage over a student that does not know GIS. It is a leading-edge workforce technology.

HOW DO YOU USE GIS TO SUPPORT PBL?

Here are some of the most common ways I use GIS to support PBL in my classes.

Collecting Data

GIS takes researching and collecting data to a completely new level for my students. Using ArcGIS Online tools, I can have students collect data by:

- Creating and adding tables information based on latitude/longitude or addresses
- Creating an editable feature service and collecting data as an ArcGIS Online map, a GeoForm, or using their smart phone GPS unit.
- Taking advantage of Survey 123 and creating their own surveys.

Analyzing Data

Where to begin? The analysis of the data is by far what sets GIS apart. Once my students collect their data they have so many options to experiment, prove, or enhance the point they are trying to make. It really is impactful for students to make simple map symbols based on data attributes to show the differences (IE. population of cities, the casualties of battles, the levels of pollution, and types of land use, democratic/republican). Many times, the symbology will lead students to ask more meaningful and authentic questions and conduct more analysis.

The analysis tools that students in my non-GIS classes use that have proved powerful include:

- Filtering data to show spatial variations based on attributes
- Heat Maps
- Interpolation
- Buffer and Travel Time Rings
- Spatial Joins

Presenting Data and Results

ArcGIS Online provides multiple ways for my students to present their research and findings in compelling and unique manners. The way that I have students present their findings varies based on the nature of the project and the time commitment.

The most common ways my students' present findings are:

- ArcGIS Online Maps with layers

- Embedding or creating screen captures of their maps and putting them in a report, slide show, or poster.
- ArcGIS Online Story Maps

WHAT ARE SOME OF YOUR BEST EXAMPLES OF USING GIS TO SUPPORT PBL?

Using GIS to enhance existing PBL activities

There are many ways I use GIS to jazz up my own or my colleagues PBL activities. Here are some examples of how GIS is integrated across the classrooms of Albemarle High School.

Using the Editable Feature Service, Survey 123, or GeoForms as a Research and Analysis Tool is not only cool, but really simplifies collaboration in the classroom. There are multiple courses taking advantage of these techniques.

AP Human Geography

Each year students research and develop a presentation on one of the major world religions. This year to ramp up the project and to help map out and highlight sacred sites we created an editable feature service in which students plot out the sacred sites for the religion a specific religion. The symbology is already pre-set to show each religion's sites in a color. As part of their final presentation students must "filter" out their religions, discuss the importance of each site, and discuss their location. This activity could be completed using a GeoForm or Survey 123.

World History

In World History I (9th grade), students use GeoForms and ArcGIS Online to collect and plot data during their archaeology simulation. They then analyze the maps to look for human activity patterns such as housing, agriculture, and religion. In World History II (10th grade), students use GeoForms and ArcGIS Online to research and collaboratively map events tied to the age of imperialism. The students also find, annotate, and embed digital primary sources related to the events they mapped. These activities could be completed using an Editable Feature Service map or Survey 123.

USING ARCGIS ONLINE AND ITS MANY LAYERS TO TRANSFORM A TRADITIONAL PBL LESSON

US Government

For years, our senior level Government classes conduct an electoral process project during the month of October to coincide with the election season. Often, they research candidates and the issues and then develop a campaign strategy and help inform our students about the issues before a mock election. Recently, some of the classes have made GIS an integral part of this project and are taking full-advantage of the capabilities of GIS to have students analyze the electoral process through a geographic lens. Here is a general overview of the GIS elements of the project.

Mapping Campaign Behavior Geoform

We created a Campaign Behavior Geoform that has project groups track and map where candidates are campaigning. The attributes they map include Date, Candidate, and Type of Event (fundraising, rally, speech, etc.).

Using ArcGIS Online Layers to Research Swing States and Swing Counties

 To understand why candidates are campaigning in certain locations you need to understand demographics and electoral history. Using ArcGIS Online layering capabilities, we built a map that contains layers on how each locality (county) voted in the previous election, and the most recent census data. Students use this map to research and assess their candidate's campaign behavior. For national elections, student groups are assigned a specific swing state and they become the experts on that state's electoral profile.

Using ArcGIS Online Story Maps to Present their Findings

 Once the research is completed and they have mapped their candidate's behavior student groups utilize ArcGIS Online's Story Map app to create an interactive multimedia presentation analyzing their candidate's strategy and campaigning behavior.

USING GIS TO COMPLETE PROBLEM BASED CAPSTONE PROJECTS

Three times a year in my GIS course I set the students free to identify a problem that they will assess or solve using GIS. I call the projects M4DM 1.0 - 3.0. This stands for Maps for Decision Making, because that is what they are using GIS for - making decisions based on the inquiry process. The parameters of the project follow the geoinquiry model and provide an opportunity to apply the skills they have been taught to a topic that interests them. Each of the 2 to 3 week windows is easily the most exciting and busiest of times in the classroom. It is also reveals the power and versatility of GIS. During any project window, the class essentially becomes a "first among equals" lab space.

Here are of the some of the types of projects that I may have running during a capstone project window:

- Map out and create density maps based on shots taken during the NBA finals.
- Analyze the distribution of EMS calls and analyze where the most calls are coming from.
- Creating a storm water tax online app so residents of Albemarle County can search for their property and learn what their estimated tax will be.
- Connect with our local affordable housing commission to create a map of affordable housing in the area.
- Using ArcGIS Online App Builder to create a college choice app in which students fill out a form to learn which college in Virginia is best suited for them.
- Using ArcGIS Online Route finder to map out a trip across America stopping at campgrounds and National Parks along the way.
- Using ArcGIS to create a Story Map about World War 2's impact on Poland.
- Using ArcGIS to create Story Map about the Rivanna Watershed. This map was selected as Virginia's entry into Esri's national Story Map contest. To see their map and all of the other state winners from 2016 Esri map contest go to http://arcg.is/1qWn1Wt and click on tab 2.

Feedback from students and stakeholders about these projects:

"The society does not have anyone on staff with the skill set to convert the existing Panama data in this compelling fashion. We are therefore grateful for the efforts of <the student> in assisting us and we owe a debt of gratitude to your institution for granting the requisite for the completion of this project."

Director, Barbados National Museum expressing appreciation for a student capstone interactive digital map display that was prominently featured in the museum's exhibition

commemorating the centennial opening of the Panama Canal entitled *"We were Giants':
The Story of the Barbadians who built the Panama Canal* "which ran from August 8, 2014 –
February 9, 2015.

"GIS allowed me to understand myself and my goals in life. I have known since I was 15 I wanted to go into Environmental Science and change the way the general public thinks about sustainability, but I wasn't sure how exactly I was going to do that. By learning GIS, I figured out how to take an abstract idea, such as the extent of damage a pipeline would cause, and make it visually comprehensible to the public. Using GIS for my capstone project allowed me to delve completely into a topic, and figure out what could & couldn't work, in a way that a one class period project would never let you do. Allowing students to use GIS for a capstone project lets them unlock a whole different way of thinking.

My favorite project was analyzing the Atlantic Coast Pipeline for any forms of environmental discrimination. Every gas company picks a path for their pipeline for a reason, but sometimes it is not completely clear what the reason is. It would be most economical to simply create a straight line, but going through the mountains (which the ACP does) can be risky. After researching it though, I found high elevations were not something considered in the construction of the path of the pipeline. It is often that companies try to place unpopular things (pipelines, compressor stations, factories, etc) in the path of least resistance, which typically refers to the communities that will protest the least, which typically ends up being minority groups that cannot properly voice their displeasure. I researched what races were in the path, but did not find that it seemed to be an issue at the census tract level. I ended up doing many more things with the project, finding new and improved ways to research. I was able to disprove a few common conceptions about the pipeline, but was also able to prove some areas of environmental discrimination. This project allowed me to tangibly view how I want to spend my future, and to that, I am grateful." - Claire M., Senior interested in Environmental Science

"The most appealing aspect of GIS is, to me, the ability to take an idea or question and turn it into tangible and more easily digestible form of information for yourself and others. GIS allows me to solve problems by looking at things from a different perspective/point of view.

My favorite GIS Project was either our Geocaching project or our storm water project*. The Geocaching project was enjoyable because I personally enjoy geocaching and wanted to create a map that would allow new geocachers to identify the highest concentrations of caches by common descriptors such as: location, terrain, and skill level. to get this map to work my partner and I had to manually input hundreds of GPS coordinates as well as descriptive data so we would have data points in the correct format to work with. The storm water project was enjoyable because it had a practical real-world connection and it allowed me to practice most of the skills I learned throughout the year. the data was available through the Albemarle County website and we were able to use that to create an assortment of maps including a density map, several supervised classifications, heat maps, and a story map using Arc GIS Online to combine them all into a presentable format. This project was interesting to me because of the possibility that the storm water fee could be implemented in Albemarle County and no one had created a way to see what the effects would be as well as different ways storm water effects the environment." - Chris W., Junior interested in Engineering and Natural Resources

"When I began using GIS I viewed it as a tool to make pictures. As I learned more about the technology and gained more experience, its functionality seemed to multiply. I began to view it as an investigative tool to explore, visualize, and model data rather than simply an image creator. Understanding how to use GIS has made me more curious about the world around me. Having the ability to satisfy my curiosities through GIS has been surprisingly rewarding and has encouraged my curious mind to wonder about more and to search for answers to my many questions. Knowing that I can answer my own inquiries and represent my findings in a way that is presentable to others is empowering. Learning to use GIS in school brought me the opportunity to have an internship with the University of Virginia which allowed me to have my work published as only a junior in high school. Unlike many of my other classes, I have already felt the benefits of learning how to use the technology we have covered in my GIS class.

My favorite application of the technology so far has been using it to analyze EMS calls within our county. I was inspired to do this project because I came across a bad map that had been published in one of the Esri map books. I knew that I could do it too...but better! I decided to gather the required EMS data from my own county and replicate the bad map project to create a thorough and cohesive map. During this project, I compared the originating location of the EMS call, the location of the responding station, and the mean center location of calls throughout the county. I analyzed the density of calls as well as the distance between the average location and the responding station in both the county and each station jurisdiction. In terms of content, my project was very like the bad map; but after I completed mine I was able to compare the two and felt proud that I had improved upon a published map." - Claire K., Junior interested in studying anything GIS

Capstone Project Requirements

Each time students complete a "decision making" project they follow the same parameters and rubric. The project with worth 250 points for the first 2 projects and 500 points for their capstone project. I value the points so high so that they recognize the importance of every step of the geographic inquiry process.

Maps for Decision Making Parameters (1.0, 2.0, and 3.0) and the rubric is available in **Online Appendix F**.

A Map Journal Story Map Teacher Guide is also available in the online resources, **Online Appendix H**.

The best advice I can give for using PBL GIS is to consider your own classroom and school realities. What is possible now? Where you would like to be next year? The year after? Integrating GIS into your classroom is a process. This was the 5th year teaching GIS at AHS and it was by far the most successful year integrating GIS in my content classes and my GIS class.

Here are my top 5 suggestions for doing GIS PBL:

5 - Don't make capstone projects one and done propositions. Find ways to make sure your students are set free to explore and tackle problems that are near and dear to them at least twice during the year. Right now, I have three opportunities and that seems just about right.

4 - Know that PBL will be new to some of your students and they may not know how to get started. I see this every year. At first, I thought students were not engaged or excited to have choice and flexibility, but the truth is that they were stuck and not sure how to get started on a PBL project. My rule of thumb for all students is that I don't expect them to know what to do, but they do need to know what they want the software to do. If a student can explain to me what they would like to do, then I'll show them how to do it or write up the workflow.

3 - Write up sample workflows to help students learn how to complete the geo-inquiry process. I do this for many projects and problems. Students just can't remember all the different buttons and steps. These are simple workflows that begin with a question and list the steps in a 1-2-3 fashion. Create and have steps for the more challenging steps on hand such as creating data sets, publishing data as a feature service, creating Story Maps or ArcGIS Online apps, interpolation, density, etc.

2 - Let students help each other on their projects. As a student becomes good at a skill or really takes off on learning GIS let them become your teaching assistants.

1 - Don't shy away from a skill or project that you and your students would like to attempt. I regularly have students ask to do a project using GIS in a way that I am unsure can be done. I am clear with the student that I do not know how to do what you'd like to do, but I am happy to learn how to do it with you. I am always amazed at how much we both learn during these types of projects.

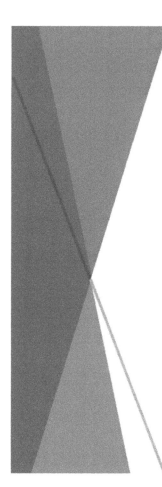

START PLANNING NOW. IMAGINE YOURSELF IN THE CLASSROOM. ANSWER THE FOLLOWING QUESTIONS.

1. WHAT ARE YOU PLANNING ON TEACHING?
2. HOW DO YOU THINK PBL STRATEGIES CAN WORK IN YOUR CLASSROOM ENVIRONMENT?
3. WHAT GIS INTEGRATION EXAMPLES SEEMED THE MOST IMPACTFUL TO YOU?
4. WHAT ADVICE FROM THE EDUCATORS IN THE CHAPTER SPOKE TO YOU AND WHY?

If you would like to practice making a story map from personal information, go to the online book resources.

8

DEFINING DIFFERENTIATION

Differentiation is a tenet of good teaching. It takes students' knowledge, understanding, strengths, and weaknesses into account. Many teachers differentiate without consciously thinking about it. As teachers plan an activity or a unit of study they're thinking about what they want students to know, to understand, and to be able to do at the end of the unit. Teachers know that students will start at different points on their journey and that not every student will get there the same way. Knowing and understanding this is at the heart of differentiation. Carol Tomlinson says that "differentiation is

not a set of strategies, it's a way of thinking and learning."
(http://www.caroltomlinson.com/2010SpringASCD/Rex_SAstrategies.pdf)

There is no single way to differentiate. Differentiation encompasses content (what students learn), process (how students learn), and product (how students show what they've learned). GIS allows teachers to easily differentiate the content, process, and product.

CONTENT

Differentiating content is about how students access and organize information. While reading is an easy and reliable way of sharing information, it's not the best method for all students. Students, especially elementary and middle school students, can struggle with how to organize information. GIS maps - regular and story - impose a structure on information that can make it easier for students to assimilate new knowledge into what they already know. For other students, reading can be a challenge that stands in the way of learning and understanding. Being able to see a map, to watch a video about a topic rather than having to read about it, to see pictures that demonstrate an idea levels the playing field for students in a way that doesn't compromise a teacher's academic goals.

When teaching history, it can be easier than it should be to overlook how geography influenced that history. Using GIS forces the teacher and the student to pay as much attention to where something happened as when and how it happened. It is one thing to tell students that the Louisiana Purchase doubled the size of the United States and it is another thing entirely for students to see that for themselves. Using Map Notes to pin links to primary source documents ties the history and geography together in ways that make it much easier for students to see the impact of one on the other.

No one way of learning is perfect for every situation. Giving students choices in how they learn required information is an important part of today's classroom. While creating maps to dispense information to students is a quick entry point into using GIS, it really is only the beginning. Do students need to understand the concept of scale or learn how to measure? To be able to compare customary and metric measurements? GIS can do that too.

How a student is exposed to content is not the only way to differentiate. Real learning requires students to make sense of what they've learned. Once students have learned the basics behind creating a simple map, they can create a map on which to take notes. If your goal is to tie geography to your content giving students the option to use a map for note taking is a natural step. Are your students learning about watersheds or river systems? Have students locate the watershed and/or river system in question and add map notes in the appropriate places. Map notes in the wrong place give teachers another way of correcting misunderstandings. Reading a story in which geography plays a role? Having students create map notes to summarize what happened in a setting or how the character changed while they were in that setting is another way of connecting literature and geography. Perhaps more importantly, it injects novelty into the concept of note taking in ways that may make students more likely to engage.

PROCESS

Differentiating process is about giving students choices in how they learn. In that respect, it can sometimes mirror some of what has already been outlined in the content section. Rather than telling students exactly what they're going to learn and the way they're going to learn it, differentiating process requires teachers to lay out options for students. There are a variety of ways of doing this.

Elementary teachers may provide students with a list of "must-dos" and "may-dos" when learning about a topic. This may include items such as: You must read this article. You must summarize the main points. You may summarize the main points in a paragraph, a storyboard, or using GIS.

Teachers at all levels may use menus to guide the process of learning. A menu gives a student a list of options that need to be completed before the end of a unit. It could be as simple as a 3x3 choice board that requires students to choose three activities to be considered complete. The menu would contain a variety of options allowing students to determine their course for the unit - reading, watching videos, writing assignments, playing games, or using technology.

GIS also lends itself to tiered activities, which are another way of differentiating process. Tiered activities are generally differentiated towards a student's readiness level. That readiness level can be a content readiness level or in the case of GIS, a technological readiness level. It can also be a combination of both. Using GIS in my own classroom, I often found that content readiness and technological readiness were not the same. By giving students different activities and options, I opened doors for students whose technological readiness was stronger than their content readiness. It is important that tiered activities are not seen as simply more work at the higher levels, but as more complex work. Using GIS as a sequence of tiered activities might be something as simple as:

Tier One: Use this teacher-created map to answer these questions. Write at least two additional questions this data would also answer.

Tier Two: Given this data, create a map to answer these questions. Write a quick explanation as to why you created your map the way you did.

Tier Three: Given these sources, determine appropriate data. Use that data to create a map to answer these questions.

While the example above does look like more work for the higher tiers, it is also more complex work. The first tier assumes little to no technological readiness and possibly a lack of content readiness as well. It is simple and straightforward, though the questions could be at the analytical level, it requires almost no prior GIS knowledge. The second tier allows students who have technological readiness and/or a willingness to take risks to try to create a map to answer the required questions. This does not necessarily require a more advanced content knowledge, though that wouldn't hurt, but it does offer more challenge to students who are motivated by technology and otherwise might not be so interested in the task at hand. The last tier requires both technological and content readiness. That readiness, however, does not need to be confined to a single student. The third tier would be a wonderful opportunity for students of differing readiness levels to collaborate to complete a challenging assignment.

PRODUCT

Differentiating product is about giving students choices in how they show what they know. It is also the most natural fit for using GIS in the classroom. Making GIS an option for a performance assessment allows students to share the information they've learned in myriad ways. Students can create a simple map where symbolization helps show what they've learned or they can create a more complex map that allows them to analyze data they've collected or located. GIS as an option is the only way to differentiate product. If you've spent a lot of time teaching students how to create GIS maps, using GIS can be your performance assessment, but that doesn't mean there isn't still room to differentiate.

Give students the parameters of the assignment: How were Civil War battles influenced by geographic features. Students can create a map using analysis tools such as buffers, they can use map notes or a story map to show the same information. Students can add videos and primary source documents to their map. Simply having students determine how they want to display the information requires them to think deeply about the question they need to answer.

Perhaps the most important aspect of a project like this is to have a driving question that requires students to really think about how they want to show what they've learned. You want students to apply what they've learned rather than simply regurgitating information.

EXAMPLES

Image 10 Westward expansion map, http://arcg.is/2smitZW. This map can be used to differentiate content, process, and product.

Content: Teachers build the map and provide it to students as one way of learning information on the westward expansion of the United States. Teachers can save a copy of this map to add additional information, such as video links or links to specific primary documents that might be digitized. Students could also be instructed to make a copy of the teacher's map to add notes or additional information about each new expansion.

In addition to simple territorial expansion, students can learn about the trails, from their length (where they can use the measuring tools, though that information is also located within the table itself), to researching stopping points along the way and to determine how long the route might have taken.

Process: This map could be used as a station or center in the classroom. In this scenario, students would either rotate to various places in the classroom or work through a variety of assignments either at their own pace or as part of a rotation within a class period. For example: students may meet with the teacher for 15 minutes, work with the map for 15 minutes, and read.

If students have some experience using GIS, they could be tasked with building this map rather than simply making a copy. A quick search for "territorial expansion" using GIS online would yield the layers used to make this map, giving students greater autonomy over their work.

This map could also be used for a tiered assignment. **Tier one** might ask students to use the data on the map to learn unfamiliar information, answer relevant questions. **Tier two** might ask students to do research on territorial expansion. Then use GIS to locate the correct layer, symbolize the layers and to write a brief description of each expansion, including when, from whom, and why it was added to the United States. **Tier three** might involve asking students to create a map that would answer the questions given to students in tier one. Directions could be given (or omitted, depending on the challenge level) for the tier two activity to help them create the map.

Product: Using the layers included in this map, teachers have a variety of options for differentiating. Students could use the trail information to create their own version of "Oregon Trail" using what they've learned about the territories and the geography of the areas through which the trails went.

- **Census Data** - Students could, given the layers, add their own map notes to create a new map that summarizes everything they've learned about the unit. Students can use symbolization to tell a story. Students could add city census data to show how the territories grew during the period of expansion.

Content: While you will eventually be making your own maps, it is easier to start with maps that have already been created when first using GIS. These are some examples of maps that can be used to differentiate content within a classroom.

- Using GIS to teach Common Core Math http://www.barbareeduke.com/ccmath/ : This is a repository of links to math lessons using GIS. Includes links to activities.
- Gerrymandering http://bit.ly/DrawingLines This map will help high school students understand the concept of gerrymandering, as well as contemporary ways of looking at the drawing of political boundaries, a profound way to talk about elections and power.
- Tectonic Plates http://bit.ly/TectonicPlates. This story map is a terrific way to engage students in the study of tectonic plates. It contains text, pictures, and video to help students understand the motion of landmasses. Students can be tasked with reading only certain pages, watching only some of the videos or being asked to review the entire story map. Differentiation made quick and easy.

Process - A sample menu is included below. Any of the links in this section could be used as part of a menu, center, or tiered activity. The Story Map gallery is an excellent resource for differentiating process.

Tic-Tac-Toe Choice Board (or menu) example for a biography unit: During the biography unit, you must choose three activities to make a horizontal or vertical (not diagonal) tic-tac-toe. *See the Online Resources for a printable version of this example.*

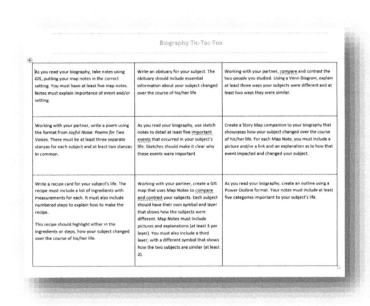

Image 11 Biography Tic-Tac-Toe handout

Product - These story maps serve as examples of maps that can be used as an option for a culminating activity at the end of a unit. Directions for creating the underlying map and story maps are included in the online appendix.

- Charles Darwin and the HMS Beagle http://bit.ly/DarwinBeagle. This story map provides a visual timeline of Darwin's voyage around the world. This kind of map can be used by students to detail important settings in a story. To sequence events as characters move about the world. Students can tie primary sources to places and events.
- Place Poem: http://bit.ly/PlacesAndPoetry This story map uses poems from the Poetry Foundation website, https://www.poetryfoundation.org/, and ties them to places and pictures from around the world. Students could write their own poetry or stories and create similar story maps.
- Ballpark Foods http://bit.ly/BallparkFoods There are times when the students get to pick their topic. The goal is to teach students how to research, how to find reliable sources and how best to present their newly acquired information. This is a good example of a project that could be given to a student that would be engaging and authentic, while still teaching the student about appropriate researching techniques and presentation ideas.
- Mary Edwards Walker http://bit.ly/MEWBiography This map is a biography of the only female Medal of Honor winner. This type of assignment would be appropriate at the end of a unit about biographies or autobiographies. Students would be tasked with creating a map that tells the story. By tying biography to place, students begin to see the connections between people and their surroundings.
- Walking Tour of the Mall http://storymaps.esri.com/stories/malltour/ This type of map has many practical uses in the classroom. This could be a product after a unit about local or state history. Students could take pictures and use map notes to write vital information about a site.

CHOOSE 2 TO COMPLETE:

1. FIND A STORY MAP AND CREATE A TIERED ASSIGNMENT FOR IT.
2. DECIDE ON A TOPIC AND LOCATE STORY MAPS THAT COULD BE USED TO DIFFERENTIATE THAT CONTENT.
3. WRITE THREE ACTIVITIES YOU COULD PUT ON A MENU THAT USE GIS.
4. USE A STORY MAP AS AN EXAMPLE OF A PRODUCT STUDENTS MIGHT COMPLETE IN YOUR CLASS.
5. CREATE A SIMPLE MAP WITH MAP NOTES THAT CONTAIN LINKS TO ADDITIONAL INFORMATION, VIDEOS OR DIGITIZED PRIMARY SOURCES.

If you would like to practice making a story map from personal information, go to the online book resources.

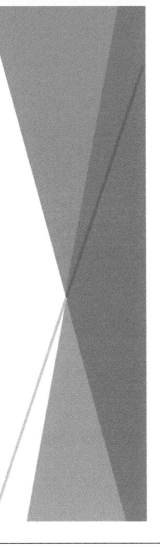

CHAPTER 9: LOGISTICS FOR INTEGRATING GIS

ELEMENTARY

You're an elementary teacher and you've decided you want to give this GIS thing a shot. What happens next? At the elementary level, you have a great many things to consider that may not apply to a middle or high school teacher:

- How independent are my students?
- Are my students able to login to an account without my help?

- Can my students type in a link without my help?
- Do my students have patience enough to wait for my help while I'm fixing an issue for another student?
- How do I keep track of passwords?

Some of the issues will be the same:

- What do I want my students to learn while using GIS?
- How can I take something I already teach and improve it with GIS?
- How do I manage everyone asking for help at the same time?

Important note: Another thing that is hard for students is remembering passwords. Because we are a Google Apps for Education (GAFE) school, our students have Google accounts, but they do not have access to email. I've found it easier to use my own school email address for their accounts so that when they do forget their password, I can reset it. When you set up their accounts, you can give them a password, but they are asked to change it the first time they log in.

INTRODUCING GIS

WHOLE GROUP

The focus of this book has mainly been on how to use GIS. That should still be your goal, but when starting with younger students, it's often much easier, and better for the sanity of all involved, if you start by introducing GIS to a whole group while you run the show. Find some exceptional story maps that will wow students and show them the power of GIS. The story maps listed below are a very small sample of the kinds of maps you'll find in the story map gallery. http://bit.ly/StoryMapGallery Find a map that will engage your students and make them want to know more about the content as well as the way the content can be presented. I would not suggest teaching students how to use GIS in a whole group setting at the elementary level. Showing them how to do something, knowing that you'll teach it again, with written directions that include images, is a great first stopping point.

Architecture, Art, and Me http://bit.ly/ArtandArchitecture This story map would be a wonderful introduction for a variety of units: art, history, science. This story map has pictures of the art and architecture of a variety of places. If science is about observations, a natural follow-up to this introduction could be to take students outside their classroom to take pictures of their school grounds, their homes, or their community and to map where those pictures were taken. Showing students how to upload photos and/or to place them on a map using map notes would be an easy whole group lesson.

Simpson's Story Map http://bit.ly/SimpsonsStoryMap This is an exploration of the Simpson's Springfield. For students, it would be a fantastic way to tie in setting and character into the concept of place. Most students do not think this deeply about setting and character when they read. Imagine the ways this could be incorporated into their writing as they contemplate how important setting and the ability to visualize that setting can be.

World Happiness Map http://bit.ly/2017Happiness The beginning of this story map offers an opportunity to discuss what makes someone happy. How happiness can be measured - or if it can be measured. Younger students could use this to create a list of things that make them happy and rate themselves. The next step might be to gather data from other classrooms or grades and find a way to map or display that data. Older students could research some of the happiest countries and those that rank lower on the scale to try to determine the many factors that fit into that ranking.

Beauty from Above http://bit.ly/BeautyFromAbove This story map could be used in a variety of ways for elementary students. It could be used to introduce the concept of bird's-eye view, the concept of reefs, or the concept of gathering data to make decisions. Students could use this as a jumping off point to determine what in their own community needs preserving and how could they go about doing so.

Expedition Palau http://bit.ly/ExpeditionPalau Breathtaking photos of a coral reef and its wildlife. The text related to the story describes conservation efforts, but the pictures would be a painless way to capture students' interests in marine habitats or other animal-related subjects.

Children's Map http://bit.ly/ChildrensMap This map doesn't fall under the guise of story map. It is a base map that was created by ESRI. The original view shows basic symbology - distinct types of trees, animals, and types of transportation. As you zoom into the map, more symbology becomes clear. It is a very student-friendly way of looking at the world. It could be used as a starting point for students to ask questions about the map: Why is this animal located here, why are the trees different, etc. Also, be on the lookout for a Yeti hiding somewhere on the map!

SMALL GROUP

You've introduced students to the wonder of GIS. They're mostly on board with wanting to learn how to use this amazing innovative technology. If you use centers or stations in your classroom, this is one of the best ways of teaching students how to use GIS without going crazy. Trying to teach technology, with only one teacher in the room, to the entire class is not likely to go well. This is especially true when working with younger students.

The beauty of GIS is that students can gain a modicum of success without much teaching. It will require having a thorough, well-organized plan and knowing exactly what skills you want students to have before you can set them off on their own.

A quick success is teaching students how to create map notes. Using a crowdsourced map, have a small group of students (actual size will depend on your comfort level, but no more than 6-7 students) working on their own computers with the map you want them to add map notes to already pulled up on their computer. You should be showing them how to do each step, using a computer screen they can see - preferably an interactive whiteboard, so that they can follow along. It's best to have written directions, complete with screenshots on how to create a map notes layer. This allows the student who falls a bit behind to catch up and allows the technologically savvy student to work at his/her own pace. Once you've taught them this skill, they can move on to an independent practice station where they continue to add map notes to a map - either the same or different. This activity does not require student accounts, only access to a public map.

Some ideas on crowd-sourced maps for the elementary set: Places they want to go, places they've been, where their family is from, where they were born, places that have a specific habitat, ecosystem, animal, geographic feature or are of historical significance.

You've taught them how to make map notes. They love it, how can they not? They're ready to create their own maps, which means they need their own accounts. Here's a quick (not exhaustive) list of small group lessons you may need to teach:

How to:

- bookmark ArcGIS Online
- Possibly related: organize bookmarks
- login
- choose a good password
- remember your password
- reset your password
- find an already created map
- access a map the teacher has shared
- start a new map

- save your map (early and often)
- save maps into folders
- share your maps with the group or make them public
- locate data and layers
- add data and layers
- symbolize data

Once you've covered the basics, you may find you have a small group of students who are ready to take more advanced GIS steps. How far you're willing to let them go will be entirely up to you and the time you have in the classroom, especially for upper elementary students. Don't assume a "smart" or gifted student will get GIS better than other students. Don't assume that a struggling student will be more challenged by GIS than others. When you bring technology into the classroom that makes learning authentic and engaging, very often those struggling students can see the implications and applications of that technology more quickly than others.

INDEPENDENCE

You'll notice that, like everything else, you have some students to take to GIS like a duck to water, while others struggle with some of the basic concepts. After you've been doing GIS with your students for a while, you'll have a good feel for who can work independently and who will continue to need help. This is where you build capacity in your students. When you have students who really get technology and are willing (and the willing part really matters) to help their fellow students, you make them your experts. When a student has a technology issue, they ask the student experts before they come to you. Students in my class liked to put up a "Help Desk Open" sign on their desks when they were at a place where they could step away from their work to help others.

Not every student is equipped to help struggling students. The students really must be willing to help, rather than do. To ask questions rather than simply answer them. For my help desk crew, I'd hold a quick training on how to help their fellow students. The best way to show students how to help in this way is to run your classroom in this way. Rather than giving students answers when they ask questions, get in the habit of asking them questions that will lead them to find the answer for themselves.

PLANNING FOR GIS

Though this has been mentioned in other places throughout the book, it's important enough to say again. Don't throw away what you or your teammates have done. Find a way to incorporate GIS into already existing projects and units. Think about what that project might look like in a perfect world. Can GIS help you get closer to that perfect world? Can you move students further down the path towards critical thinker using GIS? Ask students what they think they can do with GIS or what they want to know about GIS.

Whenever you integrate technology into your lessons, you should consider the SAMR (substitution, augmentation, modification, and redefinition) Model. A quick video can be found here http://bit.ly/SAMRBlog to explain the model, along with a blog explaining how this model matches up to Bloom's Taxonomy.

When you first begin to integrate technology, such as GIS, into your lessons you may only be substituting the technology for something you've already done. Eventually, you'll be redefining what students can do because of GIS. In the beginning, rather than having students color in countries on a world map, you'll be having students symbolizing those countries using GIS. Once you're more comfortable with GIS, students will be creating their own maps, choosing their own symbols, and deciding what belongs on that map rather than having their teacher tell them what should go on the map, in what order, and in what color. Students will be able to add videos, primary sources, as well as anything else that occurs to them to help them tell the story you've asked them to tell. That is redefining what students can do.

A powerful lesson I learned was to get out of the students' way. My third and fourth graders are just as likely to ask me, "Hey, can I do _____ with GIS?" I've learned to stop underestimating their abilities because they haven't yet reached double digits.

SECONDARY (MS & HS)

QUESTION: I'M READY TO MAKE GIS A PART OF MY CLASSROOM INSTRUCTION WHAT NOW?

ANSWER

1) Register for an ArcGIS Online account through http://www.esri.com/schools. A few things you need to consider:
   a) Who will be the administrators of the account? Registration is simple, but you'll want to reach out to your building level and possibly division-level tech support staff to decide how to set it up. If you are setting up accounts for an entire school division you will want to think through what you want to name your ArcGIS Online account.
   b) Make sure that you are enrolled as an administrator on your school account. This is a very simple process. Being an administrator allows you to troubleshoot common issues quickly.
2) Register users for your ArcGIS Online account. A few things to consider:
   a) Assign 25-30 accounts for each individual teacher and allow multiple students to access the same account. For instance, you can assign accounts as Bunin_1, Bunin_2, Bunin_3, etc. This is a nice approach for teachers that will only be using ArcGIS Online a couple of times a year. Once in ARCGIS ONLINE you can simply have the students

create a folder to store their work. The advantage is that you can use the accounts for many years for students assigned in your classes.

b) Assign all your student's individual accounts. If you take this path we recommend that you work with your administration to identify the best way to assign user ids. The advantage to this approach is that each student has a private account. The disadvantage to this approach is that you will have more accounts to manage when a student forgets his/her password or runs out of credits.

Each of the steps above can be done using a simple .csv file that contains information about each registrant. We have a starter file for you online, http://arcg.is/2y0GsSm.

QUESTION: HOW TO ENROLL PEOPLE TO ARCGIS ONLINE?

ANSWER

1) Being an ArcGIS Online administrator sounds more daunting than it really is. Here are the most important things you'll do as an administrator.

   a) Enroll users into your ArcGIS Online account

   b) We discuss this above. As an administrator, you have the capabilities to register folks in your school account. It's a straightforward process, particularly if you follow the directions to enroll people using a .csv file.

2) Decide on the privileges or profiles your students will have based on their accounts.

   a) When you enroll students, you will need to choose what type of user they will be:

   b) Level 1 - allows students and users to view content, such as maps and apps, that has been shared with them through the organization, as well as join groups within the organization. It's limited and we don't recommend it for student work.

c) Level 2 - is for users who need to view, create, and share content and own groups, in addition to other tasks.

d) You will also need to assign roles. Here are the four roles you will choose from:

1) Viewer—View items such as maps, apps, demographics, and elevation analysis layers that have been shared with the member. Join groups owned by the organization. Use network analysis and geocoding. Users assigned the Viewer role cannot create, own, or share content, or perform analysis or data enrichment. The Viewer role can be assigned to level 1 or level 2 accounts.

2) User—Viewer privileges plus the ability to see a customized view of the site, use the organization's maps, apps, layers, and tools, and join groups owned by the organization. Participants assigned the User role can create maps and apps, add items, share content, and create groups.

3) Publisher—Participants assigned the Publisher role can also perform analysis on layers in maps. **We recommend this role for high school students.**

4) Administrator— An organization must have at least one administrator. However, there is no limit to the number of roles that can be assigned within an organization. For example, if an organization has five members, all five members can be administrators. **We recommend only teachers are administrators.**

QUESTION: WHAT DO I NEED TO KNOW ABOUT BEING AN ARCGIS ONLINE ADMINISTRATOR?

Here are the common tasks you will need to do once you have your ArcGIS Online Organization operational and you have enrolled students:

- Set up your ArcGIS Online Page
  - To do this, Click on Settings -> Choose General, Home Page, or Gallery and complete your school's profile.

- o Add members to your organization (see above)
- o Assign roles. If you'd like you can create customized role for your students. To do this:
  - Click on Edit Settings -> Roles
  - Choose Create Role and decide on the privileges you would like your students to have.
- Manage Credits - credits are the currency of ArcGIS Online. Your organization will come with credits. It will use credits for GIS analysis and storage. **See Online Appendix G for the latest credit and ARCGIS ONLINE school information.**
- Three things to pay attention to:
  - o How many credits does your organization receive? Every time you log-in you can click on My Organization and see how many credits you have in the top right corner. When your account has less than 200 credits you should contact ESRI to load your account with more credits.
  - o Limit the number of credits your students can use. This is important. To set credit limits you should:
    - Click on Edit Settings -> Credits
    - Click on Set Default Allocation to give every student the same number or credits. 10 credits per student is reasonable.
    - Click on Manage Budget to assign credits to groups of students.
- Manage Your User Accounts
  - o Reset your student account when they either forget their password or run out of credits. To reset their account
  - o Click on Organization
  - o Search for your student's name
  - o Click on Action -> Choose the step you need to take:

- Manage Credits - add credits
- Reset Password - reset password
- Enable Access - give students access to their ARCGIS ONLINE accounts, if their account has been disabled.

YOU'RE READY TO START USING GIS WITH YOUR STUDENTS BUT YOU KNOW THAT IT TAKES SOME PLANNING.

CREATE A CHECKLIST FOR INTEGRATING GIS INTO YOUR SCHOOL.

REMEMBER TO CONSIDER OTHER RESOURCES, STAFF, AND SCHEDULES THAT NEED TO BE INCLUDED.

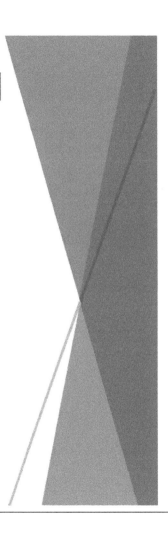

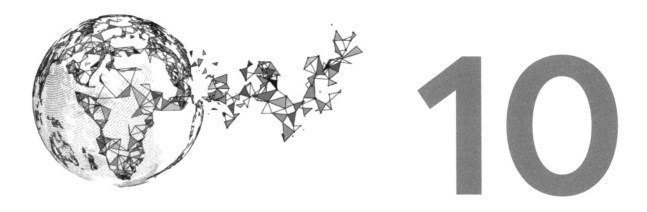

CHAPTER 10: RESOURCES

In this chapter, we provide annotated index of the myriad of resources available from the book's companion website. Our intent is to provide printed and virtual resources, which will be updated as the technology changes, for a replete solution to integrating GIS for teachers.

Accessing the *GIS for Teachers* website is easy. Open your internet browser and **go to http://gisetc.com/g4t**. The page requires a password to access it, **password: maps4thewin**. This website is home base for all updates and further ancillary materials for successful GIS integration and application. **Refer to the site often for any updates** to files, links, and additional items.

CHAPTER INFORMATION LINKS

All chapter content, that has a web link or companion resources mentioned, is cross referenced on the ancillary site, ready to click and explore. These are arranged by Chapter number. Additional resources are included for each chapter as well.

APPENDIX

- Appendix A - an example of an edited geoinquiry
- Appendix B - Exploring Physical Regions of the United States
- Appendix C - Physical Regions of the United States: Make your own map
- Appendix D - Connecting Time and Space: Who gets the rail?
- Appendix E - transportation worksheet
- Appendix F - maps for decision making rubric
- Appendix G – Esri School Accounts and Credits Information
- Appendix H – Story Map Tutorial

APPLICATIONS

Each end of chapter application is available by chapter number. These application activities are for you to practice, stretch your geospatial legs, and acclimate to the various tools and resources available.

ONLINE MAPPING RESOURCES

- GeoInquiries
- Undercover Mapper
- ArcGIS Online
- Story Maps
- Mapping Our World
- Thinking Spatially

NEXT STEPS

Now that you have completed the readings and activities in *GIS for Teachers*, where do you go from here? There are some powerful and engaging books, written by other educators for Esri Press. On the Learn ArcGIS site, https://learn.arcgis.com/en/. The following four titles are available in digital format for free:

- *The ArcGIS Book: 10 Big Ideas about Applying the Science of Where*
- *Instructional Guide for The ArcGIS Book: Companion to The ArcGIS Book*, this book provides students and teachers with additional activities, resources, lessons and data.
- *The ArcGIS Imagery Book* - Explore how imagery and remote sensing power modern GIS.
- *Instructional Guide for The ArcGIS Imagery Book* Companion to The ArcGIS Imagery Book, this book provides students and teachers with additional activities, resources, lessons and data.

ADVANCED GIS TUTORIALS

Making Spatial Decisions Using GIS and Remote Sensing

Making Spatial Decisions Using GIS and Remote Sensing is the first workbook to highlight the image processing capabilities inherent in ArcGIS software.

Making Spatial Decisions Using GIS and Lidar

The third book in the Making Spatial Decisions series, Making Spatial Decisions Using GIS and Lidar, focuses on scenario-based problem solving using an integrated workflow in ArcGIS® for Desktop.

Making Spatial Decisions Using ArcGIS Pro

"How can we protect...?" "Where do we allocate...?" "What's the extent and pattern of...?" You have questions in a spatial context; Making Spatial Decisions Using ArcGIS has answers based in The Science of Where.

These titles and many other tutorial books are available in the GISetc store at a discount. http://gisetc.com/product-category/learn-gis/

WORKS CITED

(2017). (N. C. Education, Producer) Retrieved 2017, from Powerful Geography: http://powerfulgeography.org

Coulter, B. (2000). Investigating an urban watershed: How healthy is Deer Creek? In G. L. Richard Audet (Ed.), *GIS in Schools* (pp. 55-61). Redlands, CA: Esri Press.

Council, N. R. (2006). Executive Summary. In N. R. Council, *Learning to Think Spatially* (pp. 3-6). Washington, DC: The National Academies Press. doi:10.17226/11019

Crockett, L. W. (2016, August 2). *The Critical 21st Century Skills Every Student Needs and Why.* Retrieved from https://globaldigitalcitizen.org/21st-century-skills-every-student-needs

Duke, B. A. (2010). *Reading, Writing and Thinking around the Globe.* Dallas, Texas: Carte Diem Press.

Esri. (2003). *Geographic Inquiry: Thinking Geographically.* Retrieved 2017, from https://docs.google.com/viewer?url=http%3A%2F%2Fwww.esri.com%2FIndustries%2Fk-12%2Feducation%2F~%2Fmedia%2FFiles%2FPdfs%2Findustries%2Fk-12%2Fpdfs%2Fgeoginquiry.pdf

Esri. (2017). *What is GIS?* Retrieved May 23, 2017, from http://www.esri.com/what-is-gis

Gao, P., Choy, D., Wong, A. F., & Wu, J. (2009). Developing a better understanding of technology-based pedagogy. *Australasian Journal of Educational Technology*, 714-730.

GeoCapabilities. (2013). (A. o. Geographers, Producer) Retrieved 2017, from GeoCapabilities: http://geocapabilities.org

Hanson, S. (2004). Who are "we"? An important question for geography's future. *Annals of the Association of American Geographers, 94*(4), 715-711.

Lockhart, P. (2017). *Arithmetic.* Cambridge, MA: Harvard University Press.

Malone, L., Palmer, A. M., & Voigt, C. L. (2008). *Mapping Our World Using GIS: Our World Education, Level 2.* Redlands, CA: Esri Press.

Napoleon, E. J., & Brook, E. A. (2008). *Thinking Spatially Using GIS: Our World GIS Education, Level 1.* Redlands, CA: Esri Press.

NCGE, A. a. (1985). *Guidelines for Geographic Education - Elementary and Secondary Schools.* Washington D.C.: Association of American Geographers .

Sneed, O. (2016, May 9). *Integrating Technology with Bloom's Taxonomy.* Retrieved from https://teachonline.asu.edu/2016/05/integrating-technology-blooms-taxonomy/

(2012). *Why Geography is Important (2nd Edition).* Texas State University - San Marcos, Department of Geography. Gilbert M Grosvenor Center for Geographic Education.

PERMITTED USES, PROHIBITED USES AND LIABILITY LIMITATIONS

use the digital materials provided, whether in digital or tangible form, except in conjunction with the exercises and context of this book.

You may not create any derivative works from the digital materials, except for your own noncommercial use in your classroom in conjunction with the exercises and context of this book, as provided herein.

Limitation of Carte Diem Press's Liability - As outlined in the metadata for each map document and layer package stored on ArcGIS Online, Carte Diem Press as an entity of Critical Think Inc., shall not be liable for direct, indirect, special, incidental, or consequential damages related to use of the digital materials, even if Carte Diem Press as an entity of Critical Think Inc., is advised of the possibility of such damage. Any data used is posted specifically for use with Mapping U.S. History with GIS lessons and is meant for educational purposes only.

Carte Diem Press, A division of Critical Think, Inc. 6/1/2017

Chris Bunin teaches Social Studies and Geospatial Technologies at Albemarle High School in Charlottesville, Virginia. He is also Assistant Professor of Geography at Piedmont Virginia Community College and the Geospatial Technologies chairperson for the Virginia Geographic Alliance. From 2006-2012 he worked as the Director of Teacher Scholar Programs for The Virginia Experiment and America on the World Stage Teaching American History Projects. As director, he coordinated and implemented inquiry-based experiential professional development opportunities for local history teachers.

Chris was named the 2016 Secondary Social Studies Teacher of the Year by the National Council for the Social Studies, and received the 2017 Brunn Creativity Award for the Outstanding Teaching of Geography from the National Council for Geographic Education (NCGE). Along with numerous articles and lessons on integrating geospatial technologies and inquiry into the social studies classroom, he co-authored Carte Diem Press' award-winning book, *Jamestown to Appomattox: Mapping US History using* GIS. When he is not teaching or mining GIS data, Chris can be found hiking and enjoying the Blue Ridge Mountains with his wife, Elizabeth and their 3 children. Finally, Chris gives special acknowledgement to Dr. Robert Kolvoord, Katheryn Keranen, and Paul Rittenhouse and his GIS students. "My ability to weave GIS tools across the curriculum that mirror classroom realities directly reflects their mentorship and my students' willingness to take risks."

Christine Esposito is a gifted specialist at Johnson Elementary School in Charlottesville City Public Schools. During her time in Charlottesville she has taught history and language arts to fifth and sixth graders and now teaches language arts and math to K-4 students. She participated in Mapping the Constitutional Convention, Using Primary Sources in the Classroom, and Comparing the English Civil Wars and the American Revolution. She won the 2009 Gilder-Lehman History Teacher of the Year Award for the State of Virginia.

Christine was named an NCGE Distinguished K-12 teacher in 2015 and co-authored Carte Diem Press' award-winning book, *Jamestown to Appomattox: Mapping US History using GIS*. Her current interests include incorporating history and GIS into language arts and math at every opportunity, teaching students to think critically and ask tough questions, giving students autonomy in the classroom, medieval English history, and using Twitter (@espolearns) to learn from other educators. Originally from Long Island, New York, she currently resides in Charlottesville, Virginia.

Barbaree Duke is veteran classroom teacher and an educational consultant with GISetc. She has been integrating GIS into her the classroom since 2000, in English Language Arts in grades 6-12 and other core subjects. Barbaree also serves as the Managing Editor and Executive Webinar Producer at Directions Magazine. Barbaree earned her Bachelor's degree in Secondary Education with a concentration in English at Baylor University and taught for 15 years in Texas, Alabama, and North Carolina. Along with numerous articles and lessons on integrating geospatial technologies into the classroom such as: Chapter 7 – "GIS Goes around the World in 80 Days" in National Geographic's Investigating Your World with My World GIS, Companion Lessons for *Understanding the Changing Planet,* and, most recently, several of Esri's American Literature GeoInquiries™, she's authored two other books: *20 Minute GIS for Young Explorers* as well as a solo work, *Reading, Writing and Thinking around the Globe: Geospatial Technologies for English Language Arts and Beyond.* She also has many free resources on her website, www.barbareeduke.com. When she's not webinaring, travelling, blogging, or creating, you'll find her tutoring students in reading and math most weekday afternoons from her home base in Covington, LA where she and her husband parent two amazing rescue dogs.

Anita Palmer is the president and owner of Critical Think Inc., dba GISetc that has been an education business partner of Esri since 2001. As co-author of the original *Mapping our World: GIS Lessons for Educators* book and subsequent editions and revisions over the past fifteen years, she has developed the exemplar materials for GIS integration in the 6-12 classroom. She collaborated in 2000 to develop a week-long summer institute model for GIS integration into the K-12 GIS classroom and subsequently published a nationally recognized five-year survey and article on PD best practices predicated on that training model with Kerski and Baker. Anita Palmer is recognized in the field for her work as a trainer for the Teachers Teaching Teachers (T3G) institute on the Esri campus since 2009 to current and has been an author for four of the GeoInquiry teams including U.S. History, World History, Elementary and Earth Science collections. When not mapping for work, Anita is sharing her love of mapping and travel with her husband and business partner Roger and their 23 nieces and nephews.

CARTE DIEM PRESS
map the day

LEARN ABOUT OTHER TITLES
BY OUR AUTHORS
AT CARTEDIEMPRESS.COM